Friction and Wear
of Materials

WILEY SERIES ON THE SCIENCE AND TECHNOLOGY OF MATERIALS

Advisory Editors: J. H. Hollomon, J. E. Burke, B. Chalmers, R. L. Sproull, A. V. Tobolsky

Friction and Wear
of Materials

Ernest Rabinowicz
DEPARTMENT OF MECHANICAL ENGINEERING
MASSACHUSETTS INSTITUTE OF TECHNOLOGY

JOHN WILEY & SONS

New York • Chichester • Brisbane • Toronto

Preface

For many centuries the theory of the friction process has been several steps behind the practice of finding suitable materials and lubricants for sliding applications. In the past few years, however, theory has caught up with practice; and now indeed, when present-day technology is faced with the need to operate sliding systems under conditions that are becoming more and more unconventional, so that trial-and-error testing is becoming more and more difficult, theory is beginning to lead practice.

This book is an account of the modern theory of mechanical surface interactions insofar as it explains the observed laws of friction, of wear, of boundary lubrication, and of adhesion. At the same time it is an evaluation of those *material* properties which, under specified conditions, cause one material to be a better bearing material than another. I have tried to cover my main topics at approximately the same technical level, which sometimes has kept me well within the boundary of what is known, at other times has taken me to the edge of present-day surmizing.

Although the subject of friction is a very ancient one, it remains a highly controversial one, and there are few statements that can be made in this field which will find no opposition. An examination of the recent technical literature will show, however, that the "adhesion plus plastic deformation" theory, first enunciated in the late 1930's, has been almost universally accepted by modern workers in the field; and the latest research work, although leading to a number of important modifications of the theory, has suggested neither the need for, nor the advantage of, abandoning it.

Unfortunately, the theory is silent about the question of materials. Indeed, taken at its face value, it suggests that any bearing material is as good as any other. In this respect, therefore, we have to venture along less firmly trodden paths. The criterion of surface and interfacial energy, which was arrived at by a number of research workers in the 1950's, and with which much of my own recent work has been concerned, seems to be the only reliable guide, and I have used it widely in my presentation. A number of these applications of surface energy criteria have not previously been published.

When we turn to a consideration of the wear process, which for many purposes may be regarded as a series of accidents accompanying sliding, we have an easier task than in the case of friction. Because few reliable wear measurements were carried out until recently, the dead weight of inexplicable data and of contradictory theory is far lighter, and a coherent yet relatively uncontroversial account is possible.

The organization of the book is straightforward. First comes a simple account of the relevant properties of materials and surfaces. Then follow descriptions of the phenomena of friction and of wear, a discussion of the role of lubricants, and a brief description of adhesion. I have tried wherever possible to discuss the types of experimental measurements which can usefully be made in investigating various problems, without describing in detail any particular pieces of hardware. Two types of readers have been kept in mind: the research worker who is active or intends to become active in this field, and the practicing engineer who has encountered a friction or wear problem and hopes to solve it as expeditiously as possible.

It is a pleasure to express my thanks to the many people who have been of assistance to me in the preparation of this book. I wish to thank Professor Brandon G. Rightmire for his friendly and helpful direction, over many years, of M.I.T.'s Surface Laboratory, where this volume was prepared. My colleague Professor George S. Reichenbach has been of assistance with many valuable comments. My friends in industry—too numerous to mention individually—have kept me aware of meaningful technological applications and problems. The students of subject 2.865 T at M.I.T., of whom Mr. Stephen Malkin deserves special mention, have made useful suggestions in regard to the manuscript, while Miss Rose Messoumian has been helpful in typing it. Lastly, I wish to thank my wife Ina and my family, who have been very forbearing on the numerous occasions when my preoccupation with my book inconvenienced them.

ERNEST RABINOWICZ

Cambridge, Massachusetts
October, 1964

Contents

1

Introduction

1.1 Surface Interactions

We live in a solid world. The earth itself is solid, the stones and sand on its surface are solid, man and his tools and his machines are solid. These solids are in contact with each other. Whenever two solids touch each other so that forces of action and reaction are brought into play, the solids may be said to undergo a surface interaction.

Although a surface interaction is an important and complex process, we tend to take it for granted because we are so familiar with it. Let us perform a hypothetical surface interaction experiment, in which a compact object, which may be a stone, a paper clip or a book, is placed on an extended surface, which may be the ground or a desk top. After a few moments, the object is lifted off again.

Now we know a number of things about the interaction. First, during the interaction the object was at rest on the surface, and hence it is clear that the total reaction force transmitted across the interface was equal to the weight of the object. If the interface was not horizontal, then that reaction force must have been made up of a normal component equal to $L \cos \theta$ and a tangential component equal to $L \sin \theta$ (Fig. 1-1). Clearly, the surface interaction must have been sufficiently great to allow forces of this magnitude to be transmitted across the interface of contact.

Next, we may note that to break contact by lifting the object off the surface it was not necessary to exert any force larger than the weight of the object itself. Hence, there could have been no adhesional effects during the surface interaction.

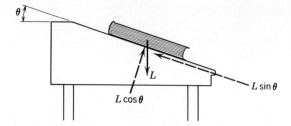

Fig. 1.1.   Forces at the interface when a book lies on a desk.

Finally, it is of interest to consider the appearance of the two bodies after the interaction.   There is no evidence, even after careful inspection, that the shape of either the compact object or the extended surface has been changed or distorted in any way, or that bits of matter have been transferred from one body to the other.   Again, these are characteristic features of surface interactions, as we generally think of them.

When considered in this way, it is evident that surface interactions constitute a very dull topic, since nothing unusual or exciting seems to happen.   Hence the neglect of surface interactions on the part of scientists and engineers of the past becomes understandable; they had more interesting things to examine.   It is now known, however, that every one of the foregoing observations as being characteristic of surface interactions is, strictly speaking, untrue.   The object was never perfectly at rest on the extended surface, adhesional effects were present, and there must have been some surface damage and material transfer.   The magnitude of these interaction effects is generally small, and in a few cases may even be at the limit of resolution of our measuring techniques, but at other times these interaction effects (namely friction, adhesion, and wear) become very large and quite complex and completely change the progress of the interaction.   Under normal conditions, the surface interaction behavior remains simple, and it is only under unusual conditions that unusual interaction phenomena become prominent.   It is a feature of modern engineering development, however, that these unusual conditions are encountered more and more frequently; hence a new look at surface interaction effects is very much in order.

Surface interaction phenomena are important in a number of diverse engineering situations.   For example, the disciplines of heat transfer and electric contact theory are concerned with the way that heat and electricity, respectively, are transmitted across contacting solids.

Each of these fields enjoys its own literature, typical of which are publications by Fenech and Rohsenow (1963) and Holm (1958). In the work which follows we shall be concerned mainly with three other, mechanical, interaction phenomena, these being friction, wear, and adhesion.

The friction effects are those which arise from the tangential forces transmitted across the interface of contact, when solid surfaces are pressed together by a normal force. The wear phenomena consist of the removal of material from the surfaces of one of the contacting bodies, as a result of interaction with the other contacting body. Adhesion, the ability of contacting bodies to withstand tensile forces after being pressed together, is the third of the interaction phenomena. It seldom occurs to any marked extent and has been much less investigated than the others.

1.2 Historical Development of the Study of Mechanical Interactions

At this point, it may be of value to give a very brief survey of the development of our knowledge about friction, wear, and adhesion.* The phenomenon of friction has been the most thoroughly investigated, since it represents on the one hand a universal attribute of matter, and thus of interest to natural scientists, whereas on the other hand it is one of the most important factors affecting the operation of mechanisms, and thus becomes the concern of engineers.

It is the engineering aspect of friction which has the longer pedigree. The first practical application of friction, namely the use of frictional heat in the lighting of fires, has its roots in prehistory. The second application showing understanding of frictional phenomena, namely the use of sleds, rollers, or wheels, often supplemented by liquid lubricants, to minimize the work required to transport heavy objects, dates back more than 3000 years.

The scientific study of friction phenomena is, however, much more recent than these applications might suggest. Indeed, in respect to kinetic friction, the friction of bodies while in motion, it must of necessity be subsequent to the enunciation of Newton's first law, and hence be a product of the seventeenth and subsequent centuries.

Early investigators of friction include Amontons (1699), Coulomb (1785), and Morin (1833). These scientists and engineers hypothe-

* More extensive evaluations of the history of friction have recently appeared (Kraghelsky and Schedrov, 1956; Courtel and Tichvinsky, 1963; and Chapter 24 of Bowden and Tabor, 1964).

sized that friction is due to the interlocking of mechanical protuberances or asperities on the surfaces of the contacting materials, and in
this way were able to explain why the friction force is proportional
to the load, and independent of the contact area. This explanation
for the friction phenomenon is generally referred to as the "roughness
hypothesis." On reading the work of these men, however, it becomes
clear that they seriously considered an alternative explanation, namely
that friction is due to adhesive forces between the contacting surfaces.
They rejected this "adhesion hypothesis" because it implied that friction
is proportional to the contact area, which is contrary to the experimental evidence.

The roughness hypothesis remained the majority view right through
the nineteenth century and into the twentieth. Beginning about
1920, however, interest began to revive in the adhesion hypothesis,
thanks to the work of scientists such as Hardy (1919) and Tomlinson
(1929). By this time the science of surface chemistry was well
developed, thanks to the work of Langmuir and others in the early
twentieth century (Suits, 1961), and it became readily possible to
examine the frictional properties of surfaces with different degrees of
contamination. The large differences of friction produced by varying
the contamination seemed more easily explicable in terms of an
adhesion hypothesis, rather than a roughness hypothesis. But the
problem still remained that, in disagreement with experiment, an
adhesion hypothesis required a friction force proportional to the area
of contact.

These difficulties were cleared up, around 1940, by three different
groups of research workers, with widely different backgrounds, namely
Holm (1938), who was studying the properties of electric contacts,
Ernst and Merchant (1940), who were investigating the metal cutting
process, and Bowden and Tabor (1942), who had experience in surface
chemistry. These workers pointed out that there was a crucial difference between the apparent and the real areas of contact, and that it
was the real area alone which determined the magnitude of the friction
force. Since the real area could be shown to be proportional to the
load and independent of the apparent area, the adhesion hypothesis
was now able to explain the experimental result that the friction
force is independent of the (apparent) surface area.

Since that time, there has been a steady increase of interest in the
friction process and detailed studies of the way the friction force is
produced. The real area of contact is made up of a large number of
small regions of contact, or "junctions," and many studies, both
theoretical and experimental, have been carried out to examine the

size, shape, strength, deformation, and life cycle of the junctions. As a consequence of this work, it has proved both necessary and possible to modify the adhesion hypothesis, so that a reasonably comprehensive body of knowledge is now available.

It is a fact, both amusing and amazing, that this development of friction theory has passed almost unnoticed by the research workers and teachers in the field of mechanics. They still cling to the roughness hypothesis, to the point where a "smooth" surface is synonymous with a "frictionless" surface. All this in spite of the fact that in 1955, Bailey and Courtney-Pratt showed that atomically smooth surfaces of mica, produced by cleavage, showed very high friction.

The histories of wear and of adhesion may be presented in very short form, for although the phenomena must have been first observed many, many years ago, their systematic study is far more recent. In the case of wear, an upsurge of interest is associated with the late 1940's, when, as a by-product of the nuclear age, radioisotopes of the common engineering metals became available, making it possible to study wear while it is happening, rather than by before-and-after measurements. It must be stated, however, that the number of workers in this field has remained surprisingly small, in comparison with the great economic importance of the wear process.

Much of the early work in adhesion was carried out primarily to study the way that surface interactions occur, in the hope that this would increase knowledge of the friction process (e.g., McFarlane and Tabor, 1950). To some extent this is also true of early work in wear (Rabinowicz and Tabor, 1951). In the past few years, however, the amount of research effort on adhesion has increased greatly, with the realization that the adhesion process can provide joints with enough mechanical strength for many applications (Tylecote *et al.*, 1958; Anderson, 1960), and with the fear that in the high vacuum of outer space, the unwanted adhesion of metal parts in contact would become a serious problem for space explorers.

1.3 The Literature

Friction is usually classified as a branch of Physics, or of Mechanical Engineering. Wear is often considered to be part of Metallurgy. Lubrication, the study of substances which affect friction and wear, comes under the heading of Chemistry, whereas Adhesion probably belongs to all the others. The various surface interaction phenomena are so closely related, however, that it is often difficult to categorize a particular topic or investigation. Accordingly, research workers in these fields tend to be affiliated with various of the relevant disciplines, and to publish their results in the journals appropriate to those disciplines.   Consequently, the literature is very widely scattered.

Progress may be most conveniently followed through the proceedings of the meetings and symposia which are held with some regularity, and which generally attract international participation.   Many important research results are published both in the regular literature and in the proceedings of one (or more) of these symposia, a system which has both good and bad features.   A listing of important conferences is given at the end of this chapter (Table 1.1).

The two periodicals which specialize in publishing research papers in this field are *Wear* (since 1957), which is international in scope, and *Transactions of the A.S.L.E.* (since 1958), which publishes the papers presented at the semiannual meetings organized by the American Society of Lubrication Engineers.   Also in this category we might place *Friction and Wear in Machinery*, which constitutes an annually appearing collection of Russian papers, the last few volumes (since 1956) having been published in translation by the American Society of Mechanical Engineers.

Monographs on surface interactions are pitifully few, so the author of this book feels that he owes no apologies for causing overcrowding of library shelves.   A listing of extant monographs is also given at the end of the chapter (Table 1.2).

1.4   Contents of This Book

Perhaps it is fair to say that the emphasis in previous books has been to discuss the interaction phenomena observed, rather than to attempt an evaluation of material properties which will cause these phenomena to be developed.   This author believes that the concept of surface energy, recently applied to the friction and wear phenomena, makes it possible to develop parameters which enable us to predict, if only in a rudimentary way, the performance of specific materials under sliding conditions.   It is the aim of this book to apply this new concept to the various interaction phenomena.

In presenting a description of phenomena as complex and as widely occurring as those of friction and wear, an author is constantly beset by the problem of whether to try to fit all the available results into one pattern, or whether to list the contradictory data and, expressing no opinion himself, leave the reader to form his own opinion. In general, I have tended to systematize the data as far as possible, partly, at any rate, out of sympathy for the practical engineer who needs guidance to-day, rather than food for thought for the next three months.

The reader is asked to bear this fact in mind in reading this book, and also in following much of the literature in this field. Often he will encounter a situation where theory says one thing, but practical experience indicates the contrary. A disagreement of this type often constitutes a fruitful point of departure for a new investigation.

The order of topics in the succeeding chapters has been the logical one of describing first the volume and surface properties which determine the frictional behavior of materials, and then of discussing the phenomena of friction, wear, and adhesion. Lubrication has been a difficult topic to fit into this scheme, since it so intimately affects all of friction, wear and adhesion. The placing of lubrication after wear has been rather arbitrary, the main justification being that wear happens to be a useful tool for discriminating between theories of lubrication.

The contents of this book are limited to the mechanical aspects of interactions, namely sliding friction, wear and adhesion. Of the topics which are often placed in this category, lubrication of the fully fluid or of the "mixed" type are not treated. These deserve, and have received, separate coverage (Barwell, 1956; Fuller, 1956; Gross, 1962; Pinkus and Sternlicht, 1961; Shaw and Macks, 1949), and anyhow they do not greatly illuminate problems common to the other types of interaction.

Finally, a word about the notation used in this book. Because the study of surface interactions is relatively recent, writers in this field have tried to use, for standard terms, symbols used by one or another of the main disciplines, and to use, for specialized terms, any symbols not generally used by that discipline. Naturally, this has produced much confusion and little standardization, a situation which appears to be almost irremediable. All that this author has tried to do is to use a notation which is self-consistant, reasonably logical, and based on at least some prior usage.

Table 1-1. Conferences and Symposia

1937 "Lubrication and Lubricants," publ. as a book by the American Society of Mechanical Engineers, New York, 1938.

1940 "Friction and Surface Finish," publ. as a book by the Massachusetts Institute of Technology, Cambridge, Massachusetts, 1940.

1948 "Mechanical Wear," publ. as a book, ed. by J. T. Burwell, by the American Society for Metals, 1950.

1950   "The Fundamental Aspects of Lubrication," publ. in *Ann. N.Y. Acad. Sci.*, **53**, Art. 4, 753–993, 1951.

1950   "Physics of Lubrication," published in the *Brit. J. Appl. Phys.*, Suppl. No. 1, 1951.

1951   "Abrasion and Wear," publ. in *Engineering*, **172**, (1951) and **173** (1952), various scattered pages.

1951   "The Mechanism of Friction," publ. in the *Proc. Roy. Soc.* **A, 212** 439–520, 1952.

1952   "Fundamentals of Friction and Lubrication in Engineering," publ. as a book by the American Society of Lubrication Engineers, Chicago, 1954.

1954   "Metal Working Oils," publ. in the *J. Inst. Petr.*, **40**, 243–346, 1954.

1957   "Friction and Wear," publ. as a book, ed. by R. Davies, by Elsevier, Amsterdam, 1959.

1957   "Lubrication and Wear," publ. as a book by the Institution of Mechanical Engineers, London, 1957.

1960   "The Nature of Solid Friction," publ. in the *J. Appl. Phys.* **32**, 1407–1458, 1961.

1960   "Mechanical Wear," publ. as a book *Handbook of Mechanical Wear*, ed. by C. Lipson and L. V. Colwell, by University of Michigan Press, Ann Arbor, 1961.

1961   "Adhesion and Cohesion," publ. as a book, ed. by P. Weiss, by Elsevier, Amsterdam, 1962.

1963   "The Nature of Solid Friction," publ. in *Wear*, **7**, 1–222, 1964.

Table 1-2. Monographs on Mechanical Surface Interactions

F. P. Bowden and D. Tabor, *The Friction and Lubrication of Solids*, Clarendon Press Oxford, Pt. I, 1954, Pt. II 1964.

R. Holm, *Electric Contacts Handbook*, Springer-Verlag, Berlin, 1958.

E. E. Bisson and W. J. Anderson, *Advanced Bearing Technology*, N.A.S.A. Washington, 1964.

F. P. Bowden and D. Tabor, *Friction and Lubrication*, Wiley, New York, 1956.

J-J. Caubet, *Theory and Industrial Practice of Friction* (in French), Technip and Dunod, Paris, 1964.

I. V. Kraghelsky and I. E. Vinogradova, *Coefficients of Friction* (in Russian), Mashgiz, Moscow, 1962.

I. V. Kraghelsky, *Friction and Wear* (in Russian), Mashgiz, Moscow, 1962.

M. M. Kruschov and M. A. Babichev, *Investigations into the Wear of Metals* (in Russian), U.S.S.R. Academy of Sciences, 1960.

References

Amontons, G. (1699), On the Resistance Originating in Machines (in French), *Mem. Acad. Roy.*, 206–222.

Anderson, O. L. (1960), The Role of Surface Shear Strains in the Adhesion of Metals, *Wear*, **3**, 253–273.

Bailey, A. I., and J. S. Courtney-Pratt (1955), The Area of Real Contact and the Shear Strength of Mono-molecular Layers of a Boundary Lubricant, *Proc. Roy. Soc.* A, **227**, 500–515.

Barwell, F. T. (1956), *Lubrication of Bearings*, Butterworths, London.

Bowden, F. P., and D. Tabor (1942), The Theory of Metallic Friction and the Role of Shearing and Ploughing, Bulletin 145, Comm. of Australia, Council Sci. and Ind. Research.

Bowden, F. P., and D. Tabor (1964), *The Friction and Lubrication of Solids*, Part II, Clarendon Press, Oxford.

Coulomb, C. A. (1785), The Theory of Simple Machines (in French), *Mem. Math. Phys. Acad. Sci.*, **10**, 161–331.

Courtel, R., and L. M. Tichvinsky (1963), A Brief History of Friction, *Mech. Eng.*, **85**, No. 9, 55–59, and **85**, No. 10, 33–37.

Ernst, H., and M. E. Merchant (1940), Surface Friction between Metals—A Basic Factor in the Metal Cutting Process, Proc. Special Summer Conf. Friction and Surface Finish, M.I.T., 76-101.

Fenech, H. and W. M. Rohsenow (1963), Prediction of Thermal Conductance of Metallic Surfaces in Contact, *J. Heat Transfer*, **85C**, 15–24.

Fuller, D. D. (1956), *Theory and Practice of Lubrication for Engineers*, Wiley, New York.

Gross, W. A. (1962), *Gas Film Lubrication*, Wiley, New York.

Hardy, W. B., and J. K. Hardy (1919) Note on Static Friction and on the Lubricating Properties of Certain Chemical Substances, *Phil. Mag.* 6th Series, **38**, 32–48.

Holm, R. (1938), The Friction Force Over the Real Area of Contact (in German), *Wiss. Veröff. Siemens-Werk*, **17**, No. 4, 38–42.

Holm, R. (1958), *Electric Contacts Handbook*, Springer, Berlin.

Kraghelsky, I. V., and V. S. Schedrov (1956), *Evolution of the Science of Friction* (in Russian), Akad. Nauk SSSR, Moscow.

McFarlane, J. S., and D. Tabor (1950), Adhesion of Solids and the Effect of Surface Films, *Proc. Roy. Soc.* A, **202**, 224–243.

Morin, A. (1833), New Friction Experiments carried out at Metz in 1831–1833 (in French), *Mem. Acad. Sci.*, **4**, 1–128, 591–696.

Pinkus, O., and B. Sternlicht (1961), *Theory of Hydrodynamic Lubrication*, McGraw Hill, New York.

Rabinowicz, E., and D. Tabor (1951), Metallic Transfer between Sliding Metals: An Autoradiographic Study, *Proc. Roy. Soc.* A, **208**, 455–475.

Shaw, M. C., and F. Macks (1949), *Analysis and Lubrication of Bearings*, McGraw-Hill, New York.

Suits, C. G. editor (1961), *The Collected Works of Irving Langmuir V.9—Surface Phenomena*, Pergamon, New York.

Tomlinson, G. A. (1929), A Molecular Theory of Friction, *Phil. Mag.* 7th Series, **7**, 905–939.

Tylecote, R. F., D. Howd, and L. E. Furmidge (1958), The Influence of Surface Films on the Pressure Welding of Metals, *Brit. Welding J.*, **5**, 21–38.

2

Material Properties Which Influence Surface Interactions

2.1 Introduction

Even to one with but the most casual acquaintance with friction and wear behavior, it is intuitively obvious that these processes are complex, and hence it is reasonable to suppose that the surface interaction properties are not fundamental, in the sense that Young's modulus for example is fundamental, but rather that they are determined by a combination of a number of more fundamental properties of the contacting materials. In fact one aim, perhaps the most important aim, of research in the friction and wear fields, is precisely that of determining the nature of this dependence, so that the surface interaction behavior may be predicted from a knowledge of the more fundamental properties. Although this aim has not yet been achieved, a fair amount of progress has been made, and we do have a good comprehension of just which are the important properties determining surface interaction behavior.

As might have been anticipated, the parameters which govern surface interaction behavior fall into two categories, namely the volume properties which relate to the contacting bodies as a whole, and the surface properties which determine the contacting interface of these bodies.

Among the volume properties, the most important, as we shall see later, are the plastic strength parameters of yield strength and penetration hardness. Then come the elastic parameters of Young's modulus, shear modulus, and stored elastic energy. Also important are parameters which indicate the brittleness or otherwise of the bodies, for example the ratio of fracture stress in tension to yield stress in compression, or the amount of plastic deformation in tension which the material can withstand. The thermal properties become important when sliding takes place at high speeds.

Among the surface properties, mention must first be made of the chemical reactivity, or the tendency of the surface to acquire a surface film of different chemical composition than that of the substrate. Of almost equal importance is the tendency of the bodies to adsorb molecules from the environment. Next we might cite the surface energy of the bodies, which determines the work we must do to create fresh surface area, while closely associated with surface energy is the compatibility of the two contacting surfaces, as expressed by their interfacial energy. These properties are discussed in some detail below.

Two important points must be made in regard to these surface and volume properties. First, it must be emphasized that our knowledge of surface interaction phenomena is still imperfect. Hence, we shall be concerned more with a broad, coarse outline of the fundamental material properties, rather than with a minute discussion of intricate aspects of material behavior, since as yet no way has been found of utilizing these finer points. As our understanding of surface interactions develops and deepens, a more complete knowledge of material properties will become relevant.

Second, it must be emphasized that a close and intimate relationship exists between many of the fundamental parameters themselves. This relationship arises from the fact that a solid is made up of atoms linked by bonds, and many of the properties of the solid are properties of the bonds. Thus, if we consider a solid with strong bonds (for example aluminum oxide), it will have all the properties that are associated with strong bonds. First, it will have a high resistance to deformation, since the bonds will offer strong resistance to being stretched or broken, and thus the elastic moduli and the plastic strength parameters will be high. Also, strong bonds will resist the disruptive effects of thermal vibrations, and hence the coefficient of expansion will be low and the melting temperature will be high.

This close correlation between many of the mechanical properties, which we shall illustrate later, has a number of important but often overlooked consequences. The first of these is in regard to the correlation between fundamental properties and surface interaction behavior. A strong positive correlation between one fundamental property and a friction or wear parameter can almost always be paralleled by an equally strong correlation with some other fundamental property

(Spurr and Newcomb, 1957). Naturally, under these circumstances it is not easy to find *the* cause for the observed effect, so as to discriminate between alternative hypotheses, for example.

Furthermore, the close relationship between the fundamental parameters imposes severe restrictions on the kinds of materials which exist, and whose special properties can be made use of by a design engineer working on a friction or wear problem. Thus, it is not possible to find a soft metal with a high melting point, even though this would make a very versatile solid film lubricant; alternatively, it is not possible to find a hard metal with a low surface energy, although such a metal would have outstanding resistance to galling during sliding.

This factor of correlation between material properties imposes limitations on our attempts to make practical use of friction and wear theory, by using theory to select materials with ideal combinations of properties, far superior to those discovered by the more normal trial-and-error methods. Often these ideal materials do not exist. Naturally the design engineer does have some scope in selecting his materials, since the correlation between parameters is seldom perfect, and there may be a fairly wide variation or difference in important properties between one material and another. But these variations are not as great as we would like.

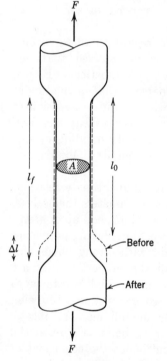

Fig. 2.1. A tensile specimen during a tensile test.

2.2 Elastic Properties of Materials

The reader is doubtless familiar with the simple tensile test in which a material in the form of a round rod with enlarged ends is stretched at a slow, steady rate, and the tensile force as well as the extension are monitored (Fig. 2.1). The force divided by the cross-sectional area at any instant gives the tensile stress, whereas the lengthening of the rod divided by the original length gives the engineering strain. The sum of the incremental strains gives the real strain, which at small

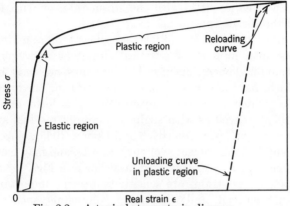

Fig. 2.2. A typical stress-strain diagram.

total strains is almost identical with the engineering strain (see for example Crandall and Dahl, 1959). Thus, for the stress we write

$$\sigma = \frac{F}{A} \tag{2.1}$$

For the engineering strain, we have

$$\epsilon_e = \frac{\Delta l}{l_0} = \frac{l_f - l_0}{l_0} \tag{2.2}$$

and for the real strain

$$\epsilon = \int_{l_0}^{l_f} \frac{dl}{l} = \ln \frac{l_f}{l_0} \tag{2.3}$$

A typical stress-strain curve for a metal, or for many non-metals, is shown in Fig. 2.2. This curve has two characteristic regions, an initial straight, steep-sloped one, known as the elastic region, and a subsequent curved, less sloping section, known as the plastic region. If a tensile test is interrupted at any point in the plastic region and the tensile load reduced, the stress-strain curve takes the path shown in the figure, and on subsequent reloading, there is again an initial elastic region followed by a plastic region.

Within the elastic region, from O to A, most materials behave as good approximations of perfectly linear elastic materials. Thus the slope of the curve from O to A is very nearly constant, being known as the Young's modulus E, and when the load is removed the specimen returns to its original length. The shape of the stress-strain curves varies little with the strain rate, or with the size and shape of the tensile specimens.

Exceptions to this perfect elastic concept of a material become important in a number of practical situations, however. Thus, in rolling contact devices, such as ball bearings, we may become concerned with slight departure from linearity during the loading-unloading cycle (which constitutes hysteresis, or a form of energy loss, Tabor, 1956) as well as with slight amounts of residual strain within the elastic range (Muir, Averbach and Cohen, 1955), since this causes a detrimental change of shape of our material, and may hasten fatigue. These effects, greatly exaggerated, are shown in Figs. 2.3 and 2.4.

Effects such as strain-rate sensitivity become important with soft metals such as lead, and with many non-metals, such as polymers. The strain rate in a tensile test, about 10^{-2}/sec, is several orders of magnitude smaller than the strain rate during sliding, which may be of the order of magnitude of 10^2/sec. Soft metals are likely to be stronger during a test at high strain rate, than during testing at low strain rates, when creep effects show up. Thus, the strength of these metals is greater during sliding than during static testing, and there

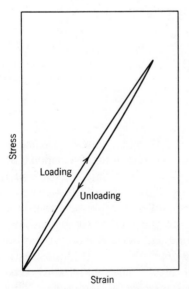

Fig. 2.3.   Stress-strain curve showing hysteresis during loading-unloading cycle.

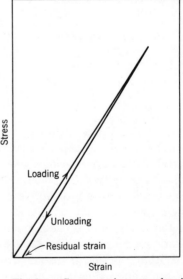

Fig. 2.4.   Stress-strain curve showing residual strain after unloading.

is a marked velocity dependence in the value of the friction coefficient (Burwell and Rabinowicz, 1953).

In some cases, the mechanical properties of a material are a function of the size of the tested specimen. Small specimens appear to be stronger than large ones, the latter being likely to contain dislocations and other features which lead to a loss of strength (Menter and Pashley, 1959). This size effect may influence surface interactions, since the junctions between contacting solids are small, and consequently their mechanical properties may be rather different from those of the same materials in the form of large specimens (Rabinowicz, 1957).

In many situations we are interested in calculating the total amount of elastic energy which a material can store, but this can only be done after the plastic deformation properties of the material are known. We take these up next.

2.3 Plastic Deformation Properties of Materials

With most materials, the stress-strain curve shown in Fig. 2.2 changes slope rather abruptly but not discontinuously, and then becomes nearly horizontal. For many purposes we would like one parameter which is characteristic of the stress corresponding to the nearly horizontal part of the curve. The most commonly used of these parameters are as follows.

1. The proportionality limit, namely the point at which curvature is first apparent in the steep part of the stress-strain curve. Strictly, there is no such limit, since the plot probably has a little curvature right from the start, which we may detect if our measuring instruments are accurate enough.

2. The elastic limit, namely the point to which a material may be stressed, so that upon stress removal, the first perceptible amount of plastic deformation is observed. This limit, too, is strongly dependent on the quality of the testing apparatus used (Reichenbach, Brown and Russell, 1961).

3. The 0.2% yield stress, σ_y, namely the stress corresponding to a plastic strain of 0.2%. This parameter is determined by the method shown in Fig. 2.5, and is probably the best and most useful way of indicating the stress level which is characteristic of the initial plastic deformation. In the discussion which follows, we shall simplify matters by assuming that the proportionality limit, the elastic limit, and the 0.2% yield criterion all refer to essentially the same stress level, which will be denoted as σ_y.

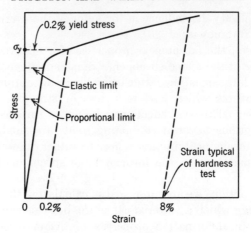

Fig. 2.5.   Relation between various yield parameters.

Another important feature of Fig. 2.2 is the slope of the curve in the plastic region, which constitutes the material's strain hardenability. A number of theories of the friction process involve this quantity (Rubenstein, 1960).

There is another method of determining the plastic yield strength of a metal, far simpler than the tensile test.   This method consists of pressing a hard indenter into a flat surface of the material to be tested, and noting the area of indentation produced by unit load (Fig. 2.6). The load-area ratio is defined as the indentation hardness of the material.

The hardness test is very simple to carry out.   The indenter may be a diamond pyramid of specified shape (as in the Vickers or Knoop test) or else it may be a ball of hardened steel or tungsten carbide (as in the Brinell test).   The load is chosen to produce an indentation that can be conveniently measured under the microscope, and then the area is calculated from the size of the indentation (Tabor, 1951).

The property measured by a hardness test is a plastic strength of the material, namely the amount of plastic deformation produced, mainly in compression, by a known force.   The hardness test differs, however, from a compression test with standard tensile specimen in that, during the compression test the deformation is uniform within the central region, whereas in the hardness test the deformation varies from point to point in the region under the indenter.   It may be shown that the deformation in a typical hardness test corresponds to plastic strain of the region undergoing deformation averaging about

8% (Tabor, 1951). The hardness value is nearly three times as great however, as the stress required to produce the corresponding amount of deformation in a standard compressive test, because the material under the indenter is prevented from deforming by the material around it, and accordingly a higher stress must be applied to push away this excess material.

The indentation hardness test occupies a central place in the evaluation of materials for use under friction and wear conditions. This arises from the fact that the geometry of a typical surface interaction, in which one surface with rough asperities is pressed against another, is quite similar to the geometry which prevails during an indentation hardness test. Hence the plastic strength parameter which best typifies the mechanical strength that a material shows under sliding conditions is its indentation hardness.

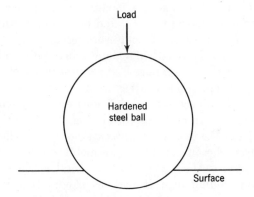

Fig. 2.6a. In the Brinell test a hard sphere is pressed into a flat surface, and the diameter of the indentation is measured.

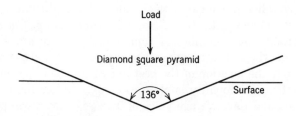

Fig. 2.6b. In the Vickers test a square pyramid is pressed into a flat surface, and the diagonals of the square indentation are measured.

2.4 Relation between the Strength and Other Properties of Solids

As we have already stated, a close relationship exists between those properties of solids whose magnitude is determined by their bond strength. A convenient way of bringing out these relationships is by a series of figures, in which one parameter is plotted as a function of another. In this section we shall present several such relationships.

First, we compare, in Fig. 2.7 and 2.8, the yield strength (for 0.2% extension) and the Young's modulus for metals. Figure 2.7 shows data for the 50 elements which are metals, and for which data are available. Because the strengths of materials cover such a wide range, it is more convenient in this and subsequent figures to use log-log plots.

Some comment for the way the data for this figure was selected seems called for. The Young's modulus of a polycrystalline metal is a structure insensitive property, and is essentially the same for the metal, in whatever state of cold working or heat treatment it is obtained. The yield strength of a metal is markedly structure dependent, however, so that the strength of an annealed metal, for example, may be only one-half or one-third as great as that of the work-hardened metal. Hence it is necessary to define carefully the condition of the metals whose yield strength is shown in Fig. 2.7. All the plotted data were taken from the *Metals Handbook* (1961), and whenever possible data has been chosen for the pure metal in fully work-hardened condition. This is the state which a metal surface might achieve after repeated sliding over it had occurred. It will be seen that most of the points in the figure lie close to the 45° line for which the yield stress is 0.25% of the Young's modulus. The data for the very soft metals show abnormally low values of yield stress because of their susceptibility to creep. At higher strain rates, characteristic of those occurring during sliding, data points would have been obtained which would have fallen much closer to the plotted straight line.

Figure 2.8 shows data, taken from the *Handbook of Chemistry and Physics* (1962) for a number of commercially important alloys. In this case, too, the yield strengths are nearly proportional to the Young's modulus, but the position of the best line of slope 45° is such that the constant of proportionality is close to 0.35%, rather than 0.25% for the pure metals. An average value of 0.3%, however, will cover both types of material reasonably well. This relation may be written

$$\sigma_y \approx 0.003 \times E \tag{2.4}$$

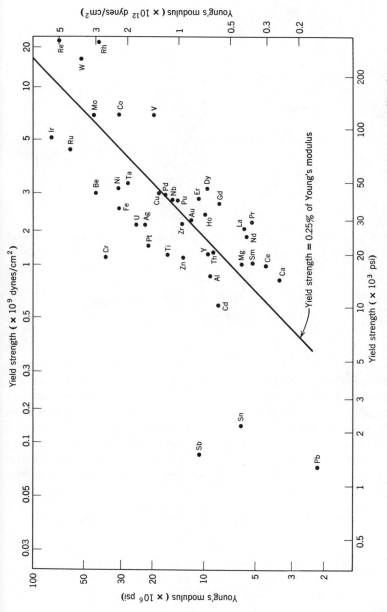

Fig. 2.7. Plot of the Young's modulus as a function of the yield strength for metallic elements.

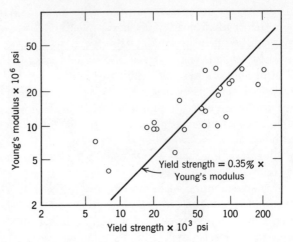

Fig. 2.8.   Comparison of yield strength with Young's modulus for a number of metal alloys (cf. Fig. 2.7).

A comparison of this equation with that which defines the Young's modulus as applied to the yield point, namely

$$\sigma_y = \epsilon_y \times E \qquad (2.5)$$

where ϵ_y is the strain at which yielding starts, shows that the value of 0.003 in eq. 2.4 corresponds to the maximum elastic strain the material can undergo.   It is a useful fact to remember that ϵ_y is about one-third of one per cent for a wide variety of metals and alloys.

The yield strain ϵ_y is an important property of a material, because, together with the yield-stress σ_y, it governs the total amount of volume elastic energy which the material can store, in accordance with the relation

$$\text{elastic energy per unit volume} = \tfrac{1}{2} \times \epsilon_y \times \sigma_y \qquad (2.6)$$

The fact that metals have such low values of ϵ_y means that the ability of metals to store elastic energy is relatively limited.   As we shall see later, this fact has important consequences, when we come to compare surface and volume energies involved in sliding processes.

It is somewhat more difficult to generalize about the deformation behavior of non-metals.   The inorganic non-metals generally fracture in tension at low values of ϵ, but they generally have values of ϵ_y, in compression, which are comparable to the values found for metals. Polymers (plastics) generally have higher values of ϵ_y, ranging from 0.008 to 0.03. A few polymers, the elastometers, have values of ϵ_y of the order of magnitude of 1, which is in the same range as the maximum elastic strain of natural rubbers.

An important relationship is that between the penetration hardness and the yield stress. Values for pure metals are shown in Fig. 2.9. It will be seen that the penetration hardness is rather closely equal to three times the yield strength. This latter relationship applies also to alloys, and many non-metals, as has been demonstrated both theoretically and experimentally (Tabor, 1951).

Next, we show the relationship between Young's modulus and melting temperature (Fig. 2.10). Even though these quantities differ dimensionally, they are closely related, and metals with strong bonds have both a high Young's modulus and a high melting temperature, and conversely. This relationship has important significance when we wish to use a soft metal as a solid film lubricant. For many applications it is desirable to find a lubricant that will remain as a soft solid over a wide temperature range, but Fig. 2.10 shows that soft

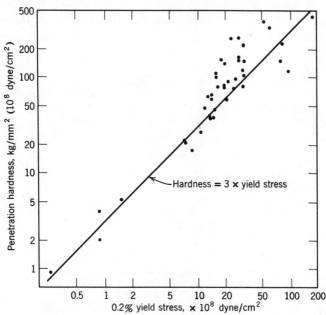

Fig. 2.9. Comparison of yield stress and hardness for elemental metals.

metals have low melting temperatures, and hence their affective temperature range is a relatively narrow one.

Finally, Fig. 2.11 gives the relationship between Young's modulus and thermal coefficient of expansion for a wide variety of materials. As Barker (1963) has shown, an empirical relationship of the type

$$E\alpha^2 \simeq \text{constant} = 150 \text{ dyne/cm}^2 \text{ °C}^2 \qquad (2.7)$$

fits these data reasonably well. Although the exact nature of the equation between E and α is empirical, we would expect a reciprocal relationship, because materials with strong bonds would be expected to be less affected by temperature, and thus expand less.

The practical importance of this relationship in the friction field lies in the properties of materials with solid surface coatings, for example a soft steel with a hard carbide or nitride case, or a steel with a soft metallic or nonmetallic coating. In neither case can we expected equal coefficient of expansion for the coating and its substrate, and severe stresses (often leading to fracture) arise when the temperature is varied.

We should not leave this section without pointing out that not all the physical and mechanical properties of solids are interrelated. Thus, for example, there is no obvious correlation between density and strength of metals, as exemplified by the quartet lead (heavy and soft), sodium (light and soft), tungsten (heavy and hard), and beryllium (light and hard).

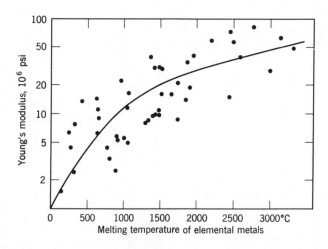

Fig. 2.10.   Comparison of room-temperature Young's modulus and melting point.

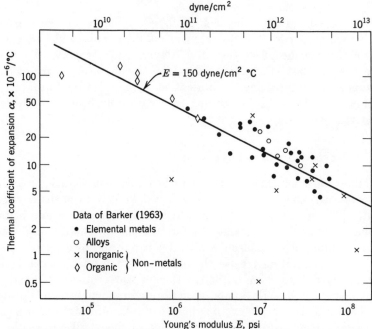

Fig. 2.11.   Comparison of Young's modulus and coefficient of expansion.

2.5   Chemical Reactivity of Surfaces

The foregoing description of volume properties has not, however, exhausted the list of quantities which determine the surface interaction behavior of materials.   Also to be considered are the properties that appertain to the surfaces of the contacting materials.   Of these the most important is the surface reactivity.

Most non-metals have essentially the same chemical composition at the surface as they do within the interior.   All but a handful of metals and alloys will form surface oxide films in air, however, and in other environments they are quite likely to form other films (for example nitrides, sulfides, and chlorides).   The thickness of these reaction products varies from metal to metal depending on the reactivity of the metal to the environment, its history, and the mechanical properties of the surface layers.   However, 10^{-6} cm might be considered to be a typical value for the thickness of such layers (Kubaschewski and Hopkins, 1953).   Only the noble metals such as gold and platinum, and alloys formed from them, are generally free of oxide or other surface films.

These chemical films have a profound influence on the surface interaction properties, but the actual effect differs quite widely depending on the specific properties of the layer. Soft, coherent coatings have the greatest effect, since they act to separate the contacting materials by interposing a lubricating layer. Hard, thin, brittle coatings tend to be broken during the load application, and are less effective.

2.6 Adsorbed Surface Layers

Besides the chemical corrosion film which forms on metals in reactive environments, there is another film derived wholely from the environment. This is the adsorbed film, which will be found both on metallic and nonmetallic surfaces. In air, the main constituent of this adsorbed film will be molecules of water vapor and of oxygen. This film will in general only be of the order of 1 molecularly thick layer, that is, about 3.10^{-8} cm, although thicker water films are found on many instances when the humidity in the environment is high (Bowden and Throssell, 1951). Many polymers can take up water vapor below the surface, thus leading to a modification of their bulk properties.

Often, there will also be a greasy or oily film, which may partially displace the adsorbed layer derived from the atmosphere. This greasy film may be derived from a variety of sources, among them the oil drops found in most industrial environments, the lubricants which were applied while the surface was being prepared, or natural greases from the fingers of the people who handled the solid. The thickness of these grease films may range from 3.10^{-7} cm up.

The presence of adsorbed films containing water and other molecules derived from the air serves measurably to reduce the surface interaction of contacting materials. The effect of grease films, if present, however, is even more marked, and reduces, often by one or more orders of magnitude, the severity of the surface interaction.

2.7 Surface Energy

Besides the chemical reactivity of the surface and the tendency of molecules to adsorb on it, which we may regard as extrinsic properties of the surface, one important intrinsic property which must be considered is the surface energy of the solids. Since considerations of surface energy have but recently been applied to the friction and wear problem, it is felt that a somewhat fuller description of surface energy is in order.

We are all familiar with the fact that liquids have surface energy, that is to say, that the surface atoms or molecules of liquids have energy over and above that of similar atoms and molecules in the interior of the liquids. This surface energy is responsible for many of the striking properties of liquids, among them capillary action, the formation of spherical drops and bubbles, and the meniscus. These are generally ascribed to surface tension; but this is merely a manifestation of surface energy, and, in fact, the surface tension (in dynes per centimeter) for any liquid has the same value as its surface free energy (in ergs per square centimeters).

Following a line of reasoning first laid out by Stefan (1886), we may make an order of magnitude estimate of the surface energy of a liquid by considering a simple model in which a molecule inside a liquid has bonds to its neighbors in all six directions, a molecule at the surface has bonds in five directions, and a molecule in the vapor has none (Fig. 2.12). To bring a molecule of the liquid to the vapor stage, we have to supply enough energy to break all the bonds, and this constitutes the familiar latent heat of evaporation. To bring a molecule of a liquid to the surface requires the breaking of but one sixth of the bonds; accordingly, the surface energy of a liquid is about one-sixth of the latent heat of evaporation of the molecules constituting the surface layer. For water, the molecules are about 3×10^{-8} cm in diameter, and the latent heat of evaporation at room temperature is about 600 cal/gm, or 2.5×10^{10} ergs/gm. From this we may readily calculate the surface energy as 130 ergs/cm^2. The actual measured value of the surface energy of water is about 115 ergs/cm^2, 75 being free energy and 40 being nonfree. The agreement between the calculated and measured values is reasonably good.

When we come to consider solids, we see that they too must have surface energy, since they too have latent heat of evaporation. In fact, their latent heat, and hence surface energy, will always be somewhat larger than that of the corresponding liquid, but in this discussion we shall simplify matters somewhat and assume that the surface energy γ_a of a solid of material a is equal to that of the liquid a at its melting temperature. This value of surface energy at the melting point is known for many metals and for some non-metals.

It is of some interest to estimate whether the surface energy of a solid affects its mechanical properties. Let us consider a simple tensile test in which we take a round cylindrical specimen of length l and radius r, which, for simplicity, will be assumed to be perfectly plastic

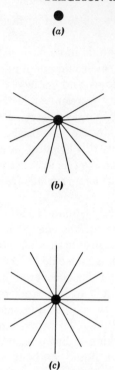

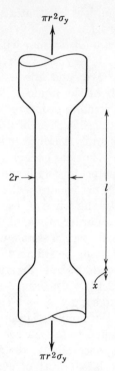

Fig. 2.12. (a) Molecule in the gas phase has no bonds. (b) Molecule at the surface has bonds to neighbors in five directions. (c) Molecule in the liquid has bonds in all six directions.

Fig. 2.13. A tensile test of an ideally plastic material.

with yield strength σ_y, and which is extended by a small distance x (Fig. 2.13). Then the longitudinal strain will be x/l and the radial strain will be $-x/2l$, since Poisson's ratio is $\frac{1}{2}$ for plastic deformation. We may write the work E_v required to deform its volume in the form

$$E_v = \pi r^2 \sigma_y x \tag{2.8}$$

and the work E_s required to extend its surface in the form

$$E_s = \gamma_a \left[2\pi r \left(1 - \frac{x}{2l} \right) (l + x) - 2\pi r l \right]$$

$$\simeq \pi r x \gamma_a \tag{2.9}$$

Table 2.1. Material Properties of Some Representative Metals

Metals	γ, erg/cm^2	σ_y, dyne/cm^2	γ/σ_y, cm
Indium	630	0.3×10^8	2100×10^{-8}
Lead	450	1.3	340
Aluminum	900	7	130
Copper	1100	13	85
Nickel	1700	25	70

The ratio of surface to volume work will indicate the importance of surface energy in mechanical deformation processes. This ratio, namely,

$$\frac{E_s}{E_v} = \frac{\gamma_a}{\sigma_y r} \tag{2.10}$$

takes on a value of 1 when

$$r = \frac{\gamma_a}{\sigma_y} \tag{2.11}$$

Thus, we see that, for specimens of radii comparable to γ_a/σ_y, surface energy effects are important, whereas for specimens of much larger radii, surface energy effects are negligible. Table 2.1 lists values of γ_a and of σ_y for a number of typical metals (a more extensive tabulation is shown in the appendix). It will be seen that the values of (γ_a/σ_y) are very small, of the order of magnitude of 10^{-6} or 10^{-7} cm for most metals. Hence we conclude that for specimens of normal size, surface energy effects are negligible.

We may note in passing that the ratio of surface energy to mechanical stress, as shown in Eq. 2.11, has the dimensions of a length. In the pages that follow, we shall frequently encounter similar expressions, where a length is equated to some numerical constant multiplied by the γ/σ_y ratio, or some analogous ratio.

2.8 Relationship between Surface Energy and Hardness

Because both the surface energy and the mechanical strength of a material depend on the strength of its bonds, we would expect that high surface energies are associated with high strength parameters. Figure 2.14 shows a plot of the surface energy as a function of one such parameter, namely the penetration hardness. Data are presented for a large number of elemental metals, in the cold-worked state, and for a few non-metals.　It will be seen that the correlation between hardness and surface energy is, indeed, a close one.

It is important to notice, however, that the best straight line in Fig. 2.14 would have a slope considerably smaller than 1, more nearly $\frac{1}{3}$.　Thus, we may write a relationship in the form

$$\gamma \propto p^{1/3} \tag{2.12}$$

This relationship is brought out more clearly in Fig. 2.15 in which the γ/p ratios are plotted against p.　It will be seen that soft materials have higher γ/p ratios than do harder materials.　Also, that non-metals have lower γ/p ratios than do metals of comparable hardness.

In later chapters we see then low γ/p ratios are associated with "better" surface interaction behavior, namely lower friction, smaller wear particles, smoother surfaces, and less adhesion.　Accordingly, for sliding applications involving unlubricated surfaces, non-metals are better than metals, and hard materials are better than soft materials.

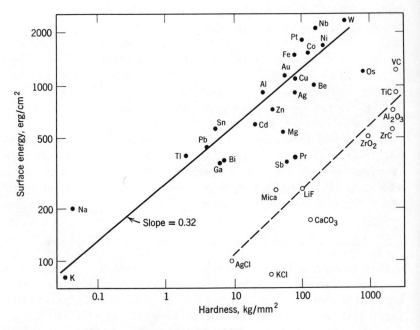

Fig. 2.14.　Plot of surface energy at the melting point against hardness at room temperature, for some metals and non-metals.

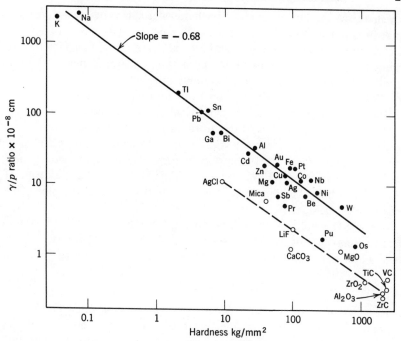

Fig. 2.15. Plot of the γ/p ratio against hardness for the materials shown in Fig. 2.14.

2.9 Surface Interfacial Energies of Solids under Engineering Conditions

The values of surface energy discussed earlier are those attributable to the clean metals at their melting temperature. In practice however, we are generally interested in the energy values for surfaces which are more-or-less contaminated, and moreover which are at, or near room temperatures. McLean (1957) has shown that surface energies of metals increase by an amount of the order 0.5 erg/cm² for every degree centigrade temperature drop from the melting point. For a typical metal, either a soft one like lead (surface energy at the melting point = 450 erg/cm², melting point = 325°C) or a hard one like nickel (surface energy = 1700 erg/cm², melting point = 1450°C), the surface energy of the clean surface at room temperature will be about 50% higher than at the melting temperature.

In air the surfaces will pick up oxide films, which lower the surface energy; however, these oxide films tend to be broken up during sliding, which raises the surface energy back toward the value it would have under oxide-free conditions. All in all, this is a complex subject, but it seems reasonable to assume that the 50% increase in surface energy going from the melting point to room temperature is matched by a similar diminution attributable to oxide and other contaminant films, so that the two adjustments cancel out and we may use the melting temperature value for normal, unlubricated sliding conditions.

Of course, if a good boundary lubricant, such as a grease, is applied to the surfaces, the effective surface energy drops to a level which corresponds more closely to the surface energy of the grease, which may be in the vicinity of 30–40 erg/cm^2. This is a very drastic drop, of course, and helps to explain why organic materials of this type act as effective lubricants.

Later in this volume, especially in Chapters 4 and 6, we shall be interested primarily, not in the surface energies γ_a and γ_b of the two materials a and b, but in the energy of adhesion W_{ab}, given by the relation

$$W_{ab} = \gamma_a + \gamma_b - \gamma_{ab} \qquad (2.13)$$

In this equation, W_{ab} represents the energy which must be applied to separate 1 cm^2 of the interface between materials a and b, involving the need to create two surfaces of energy γ_a and γ_b respectively, but destroying an interface which had interfacial energy of amount γ_{ab}.

According to data collected by McLean (1957) values of γ_{ab} seem generally to be of the order of magnitude of $\frac{1}{4}$ to $\frac{1}{2}$ of $(\gamma_a + \gamma_b)$. The smaller values are attributable to cases where materials a and b are highly compatible, as evidenced by high mutual solubility or the formation of intermetallic compounds, since in these cases the interface between materials a and b does not constitute a drastic discontinuity, and hence has little surface energy.   In the extreme case where a and b are made of the same material, we assume $\gamma_{ab} = 0$, even though there will be some interfacial energy unless the two crystal lattices match perfectly.   In cases where a and b are very insoluble, and form no intermetallic compounds, the value of γ_{ab} is quite high.   Thus we have three cases to consider:

$$
\begin{array}{lll}
a \text{ and } b \text{ identical} & W_{ab} \approx 2\gamma_a & \\
a \text{ and } b \text{ compatible} & W_{ab} \approx \tfrac{3}{4}(\gamma_a + \gamma_b) & (2.14) \\
a \text{ and } b \text{ incompatible} & W_{ab} \approx \tfrac{1}{2}(\gamma_a + \gamma_b) &
\end{array}
$$

where $\approx$ denotes "is approximately equal to."

We shall see later that high W_{ab} values are associated with poor sliding conditions. According to eq. 2.14, this implies that the use of the same material for both sliding surfaces is bad, that the use of unlike but compatible materials is questionable, whereas the use of incompatible materials is best.   This agrees with actual experience.

References

Barker, R. E. (1963), An Approximate Relation between Elastic Moduli and Thermal Expansivities, *J. Appl. Phys.*, **34**, 107–116.

Bowden, F. P., and W. R. Throssell (1951), Adsorption of water vapour on solid surfaces, *Proc. Roy. Soc.*, A **209**, 297–308.

Burwell, J. T., and E. Rabinowicz (1953), The Nature of the Coefficient of Friction *J. Appl. Phys.*, **24**, 136–139.

Crandall, S. H., and N. C. Dahl (1959), *An Introduction to the Mechanics of Solids*, McGraw-Hill, New York.

Handbook of Chemistry and Physics, 43rd Edition (1962), Chemical Rubber Publishing Co., Cleveland, Ohio.

Kubaschewski, O., and B. E. Hopkins (1953), *Oxidation of Metals and Alloys*, Butterworths, London.

McLean, D. (1957), *Grain Boundaries in Metals*, Clarendon Press, Oxford.

Menter, J. W., and D. W. Pashley (1959), The Microstructure and Mechanical Properties of Thin Films, pp. 111–150 of *Structure and Properties of Thin Films*, ed. C. A. Neugebauer, J. B. Newkirk, O. A. Vermilyea, Wiley, New York.

Metals Handbook, 8th Edition, Vol. 1 (1961) A.S.M., Metals Park, Novelty, Ohio.

Muir, H., B. L. Averbach, and M. Cohen (1955), The Elastic Limit and Yield Behavior of Hardened Steels, *Trans. A.S.M.*, **47**, 380–407.

Rabinowicz, E. (1957), Investigation of Size Effects in Sliding by Means of Statistical Techniques, p. 276–280 of *Proc. Conf. Lubrication and Wear*, Institution of Mechanical Engineers, London.

Reichenbach, G. S., D. S. Brown, and P. G. Russell (1961), Yield Behavior of Certain Alloy Steels at Low Strain Values, *Trans. A.S.M.*, **54**, 413–429.

Rubenstein, C. (1960), The Influence of Workhardening on the Coefficient of Friction, *Wear*, **3**, 150–153.

Spurr, R. T., and T. P. Newcomb (1957), The Friction and Wear of Various Materials Sliding Against Unlubricated Surfaces of Different Types and Degrees of Roughness, pp. 269–275 of *Proc. Conf. Lubrication and Wear*, Institution of Mechanical Engineers, London.

Stefan, J. (1886), On the Relation between Theories of Capilarity and of Evaporation (in German), *Ann. d. Phys.*, **29**, 655–665.

Tabor, D. (1951), *The Hardness of Metals*, Oxford University Press, Oxford.

Tabor, D. (1956), The Mechanism of "Free" Rolling Friction, *Lubrication Engineering*, **12**, 379–386.

3

Surface Interactions

3.1 The Origin of Surface Interactions

Suppose two solid materials are placed in contact (Fig. 3.1). Some regions on their surface will be very close together, others will be further apart. It is important to know which atoms interact strongly with the corresponding atoms on the other surface, and which do not. It is known that the powerful atom-to-atom forces are of very short range, of the order of magnitude of a few Angstroms only, this range being about the size of the average atom. Hence it is possible to simplify the problem, and assume that all the interaction takes place at those regions between the surfaces at which there is atom-to-atom

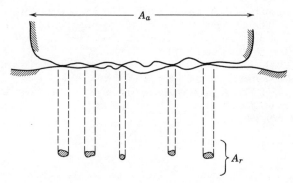

Fig. 3.1. Schematic illustration of an interface, showing the apparent and real areas of contact.

contact. These regions will be referred to as "junctions," and the sum of the areas of all the junctions constitute the "real" area of contact A_r. The total interfacial area, consisting both of the real area of contact and also those regions which appear as if contact might have been made there (but was not), will be denoted as the "apparent" area of contact, A_a.

It will be appreciated that, although those regions within the apparent area of contact at which contact is not made may be far larger than the real area of contact, they play essentially no part in determining the overall interaction. There do exist very weak long-range forces which operate at points on the surface separated by distances exceeding 10 Å, but, as Abrikosova and Deryagin (1957) have shown, it is very difficult to measure these long-range forces because of their small size $(10^{-2}$ dyne/cm^2 or less), and they are negligible in magnitude compared with the short-range forces.

3.2 The Size of the Real Area of Contact

In view of the fact that the nature of the interaction between two surfaces is determined by the real area of contact, it is necessary to derive as much information as possible about the real area. First and foremost, we would like to know the size of the real area. At first sight, it would seem to be impossible to make any kind of quantitative statement about the magnitude of A_r when two surfaces are pressed together by a force L normal to their interface of contact, without having available a great deal of information about the circumstances of the contact, namely the size and shape of the apparent area of contact, the surface roughnesses of the two materials, and the way they are placed together. Even when these parameters are given, a high-speed computer seems to be necessary for the problem to become tractable. Fortunately, we can make a very simple limit analysis and calculate a minimum value for A_r, assuming ideally plastic deformation. This *minimum* value usually turns out to be close to the *actual* value of the real area of contact.

To calculate a minimum value for A_r, we note that if the surfaces that are placed in contact are rough but not excessively rough, a typical junction will look as shown in Fig. 3.2, and, as will be really seen, the interface will be in a state of triaxial constraint. The largest compressive stress that such a region of material can carry without plastic yielding is known as its penetration hardness p, which we have shown in Chapter 2 to be about three times as great as the yield

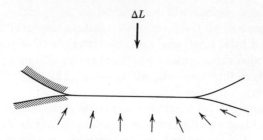

Fig. 3.2.   Forces exerted over a single junction.   Note resemblance to Fig. 2.6.

strength σ_y in uniaxial compression.   Then the value of the real area of contact, A_r, is given by

$$A_r \geq \frac{L}{p} \qquad (3.1)$$

There are a number of arguments which may be used to show that in many cases, perhaps a great majority of cases, A_r is indeed equal to L/p.   First, there is the argument of plausibility.   It may readily be shown that most surfaces as prepared technically have ridges and valleys, and thus, when one such surface is pressed into another, the geometry is very similar to that prevailing in a hardness test, but on a smaller scale.   Thus it is easy to see that as the two surfaces are brought into contact and a normal load is applied, plastic deformation will occur so that the initial contact of three points becomes eventually the contact of numerous sizeable areas, and deformation will continue until the total real area of contact reaches a value given by

$$A_r = \frac{L}{p} \qquad (3.2)$$

At this stage deformation will cease.

The second argument in favor of eq. 3.2 is based on experimental evidence and takes a number of forms.   First, we may mention the electrical resistance measurements of contacting metals made by Bowden and Tabor (1939).   This work shows that the electric contact resistance values are, in general, consistent with eq. 3.2.   Next, there is the argument that the friction coefficient of sliding materials is substantially independent of load and geometry of contact.   This is also consistent with a plastic deformation model, but inconsistent with many other assumed modes of deformation.   Last, it might be said that in some circumstances the real area of contact has been directly measured, and found to be of the same order of magnitude as the value given in eq. 3.2 (Kraghelsky and Demkin, 1960).

It is only in exceptional cases that the value of A_r becomes much greater than is suggested by eq. 3.2 so that we are forced to use the noncommittal eq. 3.1. Of these cases, mention should be made of three main categories. The first is that of surfaces where the surface asperities are very small and consequently the surface is very smooth. Under these circumstances, there may be no plastic deformation whatever when two such surfaces are brought together, only elastic deformation, and A_r will be greater, perhaps far greater, than eq. 3.2 suggests. This is the case of highly polished surfaces such as bearing balls (Fig. 3.3), which when pressed into a flat polished surface will produce an area of contact as given by Hertz's equation for elastic deformation, namely

$$A_r = 2.9 \left[Lr \left(\frac{1}{E_1} + \frac{1}{E_2} \right) \right]^{\frac{2}{3}} \qquad (3.3)$$

assuming that Poisson's ratio for both surfaces is 0.3 (Tabor, 1951). A similar situation arises when one of the two contacting materials is an elastometer. The deformation will then probably remain elastic, even when the contacting surfaces are fairly rough.

The second case to be considered is that in which shear forces, as well as normal forces, act on a junction. Although this is the most common case of all, prevailing as it does in all sliding situations, it is still not perfectly understood. It is clear that the shear force will have a profound effect on the equilibrium position of the two materials. In fact, when the shear force is first applied, tangential motion occurs even while the tangential force is quite low (Courtney-Pratt and Eisner, 1957). This motion has the effect of increasing the area of contact, which recreates equilibrium under the joint action of the normal and shear forces, so that relative motion of the two surfaces in

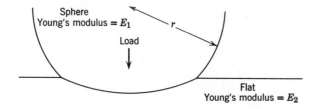

Fig. 3.3. An elastic contact.

a normal direction inward ceases.   If the shear force is continually increased, the increase in real area of contact with increased shear force eventually falls short of that required to maintain static equilibrium, and hence sliding motion will occur (Fig. 3.4).   In a typical situation, the final area of contact before sliding commences might be about three times as great as the value before shear forces were first applied.

Before we proceed to the third effect which increases A_r, namely that attributable to surface energy, it may be well to consider a phenomenon which may reduce A_r below the value given in eq. 3.2. This is the size effect mentioned in Chapter 2, which is a characteristic feature of the strength properties of metals and many inorganic materials.   The sizes of typical junctions, namely 10^{-3} to 10^{-4} cm, are on the borderline of the sizes of specimens which have been shown to be subject to size effects (Menter and Pashley, 1959).   Hence, it seems that in eq. 3.2, it is necessary to use, for the hardness p, not the value obtained under normal testing when a large indentation is used, but that which would be obtained if an indenting load was used small enough to produce an indentation of diameter in the 10^{-3} to 10^{-4} cm range.   The hardness as determined under light load testing might be larger by as much as a factor of two or three, and A_r would then be correspondingly smaller.

Closely analogous to the size effect, which operates because the hardness of the materials is not invariant, are effects which arise in materials which creep to a marked extent.   In this case, the value of A_r will

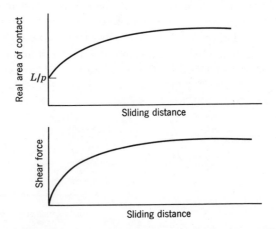

Fig. 3.4.   Variation of A_r and of shear force with sliding distance.

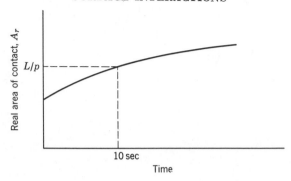

Fig. 3.5. Variation of A_r with time of application of the load, for materials which creep.

increase with time of application of the load (Moore and Tabor, 1952). In a typical hardness test the load is applied for about 10 sec, so that the hardness value may be called the "10-second strength." Thus, for materials which creep, A_r will be smaller than the value given in eq. 3.2 for the first 10 sec after the load is applied, and progressively larger than the value given in eq. 3.2 after 10 sec of load application. Eventually, very large areas of contact will be produced (Fig. 3.5).

3.3 Influence of Surface Energy on Area of Contact

In the discussion of the factors which determine the size of the real area of contact, we have so far confined ourselves to volume properties, those of elasticity, plasticity, creep, and size effect. The surface properties may also be important, however, as a simple calculation will show (Rabinowicz, 1961). Suppose we have a hard conical indenter and press it into a softer material of hardness p by means of a load ΔL (Fig. 3.6). Then we may calculate the energy change during indentation, as a result of volume deformation of the softer material (which is assumed to be ideally plastic) and also as result of the diminution of free surface area and the formation of an interface. Then we may use the minimum energy principle to determine the equilibrium position of the system. *Note:* There is no guarantee that the minimum energy principle applies to a nonconservative process like plastic deformation, but in this application it appears to give a correct result (as may be checked in the case where we put the surface energy equal to zero), because we never reverse the displacement of the conical rider.

If the rider penetrates by a distance x, the load produces energy of

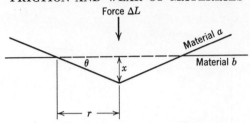

Fig. 3.6.   Hard cone of material a pressed into a softer flat surface of material b.

amount $\Delta L \cdot x$, the material uses up (in deformation) energy of an amount equal to $\int_0^x \pi r^2 p \cdot dx$, and the surface produces energy of amount $\pi r^2(\gamma_a + \gamma_b)$, and uses up energy of amount $\pi r^2 \gamma_{ab}$.   (In the surface energy terms, we have assumed that the projected and real areas of the interface between the indenter and the softer surface are equal.)   This allows us to write the overall surface energy change as $\pi r^2 W_{ab}$.   Then we write for the overall energy gain E_g

$$E_g = \Delta L \cdot x - \int_0^x \pi r^2 p \cdot dx + W_{ab} \cdot \pi r^2 \qquad (3.4)$$

If we now make the substitution $r = x \cot \theta$ and differentiate, we obtain

$$\frac{dE_g}{dx} = \Delta L - \pi r^2 p + 2\pi r W_{ab} \cot \theta \qquad (3.5)$$

For equilibrium, $\dfrac{dE_g}{dx}$ is zero, which gives

$$\Delta L = \pi r^2 p - 2\pi r W_{ab} \cot \theta \qquad (3.6)$$

If we ignore the surface energy term (i.e., if we assume that W_{ab} is zero), then eq. 3.6 is identical with eq. 3.2.   In the presence of surface energy, however, A_r will always be greater than is indicated by eq. 3.2. This effect is especially pronounced when the surface energy W_{ab} is large, or the surface roughness is very small.

3.4   The Experimental Study of Surfaces and Interfaces—Roughness

Now that we have described from a theoretical standpoint the factors which determine the surface interaction between two contacting solids, we will do well to discuss some of the main techniques which may be used to investigate such interactions.   The aim of such studies is twofold; first, they enable us to check whether macroscopic relationships such as eq. 3.2 are true, and secondly they enable us to find out something, at the microscopic level, about the individual junctions which make up the real area of contact.   This knowledge can then be put to use in a number of ways when we come to discuss the friction and wear phenomena.   First, however, we will do well to discuss one important type of measurement which describes a surface, and only indirectly tells us what happens when we put two surfaces together to form an interface.   This measurement involves the determination of the surface roughness.

The surface roughness may be defined as the departure of the surface shape from some ideal or prescribed form.   Thus, if we have a nominally flat surface, we might define the roughness in terms of the ratio of the true overall area to the nominal projected area, or as the slope of a profile taken along some prescribed line, or as the distance between high points and low points on the surface (Fig. 3.7).   Anyhow, the measurement must be made by suitable probing instruments, and the characteristics of the probe then influence the roughness determination made with that probe.   We shall consider a number of probes which operate on quite different principles, namely a mechanical pointer or stylus, a beam of light, and a quantity of adsorbing molecules.

The profile meter.   This is perhaps the most widely used method of measuring roughness, and employs a stylus, usually with a rounded end, of some very hard material (e.g., diamond).   Such a stylus closely resembles a phonograph needle (and this resemblance extends

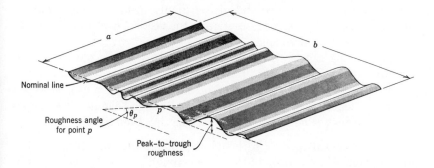

Fig. 3.7.   Various definitions of roughness.   Either: Roughness ratio, namely quotient of overall area of the surface to nominal area ab.   Or: Roughness angle θ_p (either mean or R.M.S. angle).   Or: Roughness distance (either peak-to-trough or R.M.S. departure from nominal line).

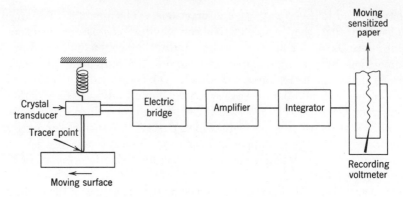

Fig. 3.8.   Schematic illustration of a profile meter.

beyond appearance since in a stereo system the needle is used to measure the waviness or roughness of the phonograph record). In a roughness measurement the stylus is moved across the surface, and its vertical movements are amplified electrically or mechanically, and usually recorded on a chart (Fig. 3.8). Alternatively, the small displacements are integrated and averaged out to produce some sort of average (usually root-mean-square) roughness value, representing an average departure of the measured profile from its ideal position.

The performance characteristics are determined by the shape and size of the probe (the radius of curvature of the probe tip is typically 5×10^{-4} cm). Although profile meters are extremely sensitive in detecting gentle undulations in a surface, they are quite poor at detecting sharp crevasses, and give a highly distorted impression of sharp ridges. Their basic resolution in the vertical direction is usually of the order of a microinch.

A promising approach would be to measure both a surface and a replica of the surface with a profile meter. In this way the crevasses of the surface would become ridges of the replica, and thus both types of surface features would be detected. Although this idea is a simple one, the author is not aware of its ever having been tried.

Optical techniques. Although a profile meter provides a quick and convenient indication of the surface roughness along one line, it is not very convenient for assessing a substantial area for departures from smoothness. For this latter purpose it is more convenient to resort to an optical technique. There are many methods of examining surfaces optically, to gain an insight into their roughness (Tolansky,

1953).   Generally, we shine a beam of light at the surface, and then inspect to see how the beam has been disturbed by reflection in the surface.   Irregularities in the surface show up as features in the reflected beam.   Of the many available methods we may mention the following:

Specular Reflection Measurement.   A beam of light is shone on the surface at an angle, and the fraction of the light that is not specularly reflected is measured.   This gives some indication of the roughness (Fig. 3.9).

Inspection of the Surface in a High-Powered Microscope.   The extent and intensity of the features observable under direct and oblique illumination give an indication of the nature of the surface irregularities.

Light Profile Methods.   In these methods an oblique light or shadow is cast on the surface, and the nature of the surface irregularities made plain (Fig. 3.10).

All the above methods share the same features, namely that the vertical resolution is no better than that of any optical system, namely $\frac{1}{2}$ the wavelength of light, and the horizontal resolution is comparable. This is something of an inconvenience, since the wavelength of light, 5×10^{-5} cm, is larger than would be desirable for studying many surfaces.   Various interference methods do exist, however.   These generally have greatly improved resolution in the vertical direction— down to a few Angstroms—but much poorer horizontal resolution.

In order to obtain good resolution in both directions, we may resort to electron microscopy.   Much important information has been obtained in this way, but the various techniques are difficult and tedious, and artifacts are sometimes encountered.

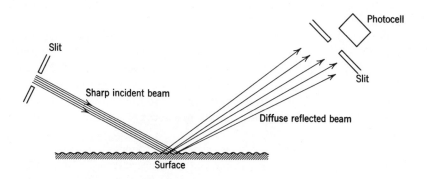

Fig. 3.9.   Reflectivity method of studying surface roughness.

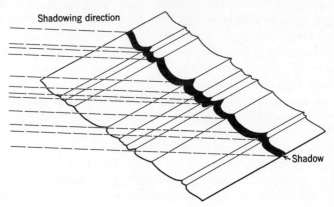

Fig. 3.10.   Light profile method of studying roughness.   This method works best when roughness consists of parallel ridges and grooves.

Adsorption techniques.   When molecules are adsorbed on solid surfaces, they are first and preferentially adsorbed on the most active sites, then on other sites on the surface, and eventually, after all the surface sites have been filled, a second layer starts to build up on the first.   From a study of the way that adsorption takes place, that is to say, from the measurement of the amount of adsorption as a function of the concentration of adsorbing molecules, it is possible to deduce at what stage the adsorption of the first molecular layer is completed and the adsorption of the second layer has commenced.   This experiment, then, makes it possible to estimate, with some precision, the surface area of a solid surface, assuming that a measurement has been made of the total amount of material required to constitute an adsorbed monolayer.

This method studies surfaces using, as probes, the adsorbing molecules themselves.   Most of the experiments which have been carried out with this method have used simple adsorbing gases, of diameter about 3.10^{-8} cm.   This probe is small enough to penetrate deeply into cracks and microcracks in the surface, and to follow the outline of fine surface features of all kinds.   This method provides an estimate of the total area of the surface.

The results obtained by the adsorption method, which are discussed by O'Connor and Uhlig (1957), have been extremely interesting. Although a typical metal surface obtained by electro-polishing or by rolling has a total surface area only slightly greater than its projected area, yet a metal surface obtained by an abrasion process has a total area nearly three times as great as its projected area. These results may be interpreted either by saying that a large number of deep cracks abound in the surface, or by supposing that the average surface roughness is that of an inclined surface whose cosine is $\frac{1}{3}$. This amounts to a roughness angle of about 70°. Observations of surfaces in the reflection electron microscope (Halliday, 1957), and inspection of traces observed with profile meters, suggest far smaller surface roughnesses, with values ranging from 0.1° to 5° being typical. This violent disagreement appears to be due in part at any rate to differences in the size of the probe (less than 10^{-7} cm in the adsorption case as against more than 10^{-5} cm with the profile meter), but the problem has still not been resolved.

3.5 Measurements of the Geometry of Surface Interactions

We have seen earlier in this chapter that the total area of contact A_r may be calculated, at least approximately, by plastic limit methods. In this section we will investigate the way that this total area is made up, as regards number and size of junctions. A number of methods have been used for this purpose. Most of them are indirect, in that they estimate the number and size of the junctions based on surface interaction effects which depend on the magnitude of these parameters. In some cases these measurements involve sliding, or at any rate vibration, of the two materials, and thus might logically have been postponed until the next chapter.

Electric resistance method. Measurements of the electrical resistance of an interface are frequently made, either for their intrinsic interest (e.g., to study the functioning of electric contacts, or the resistance welding process) or because of the light they throw on the geometry of the interface. The basic equation for the electrical resistance R of a circular contact (Fig. 3.11), is

$$R = \frac{\rho}{2r} \tag{3.7}$$

where ρ is the electrical resistivity of each material (Holm, 1958).

This result is unexpected, because we would have expected R to vary inversely as r^2. But it turns out that most of the resistance is produced near the constriction, and, if we adopt an oversimplified model in which the resistance is that of a cylinder of height r and area

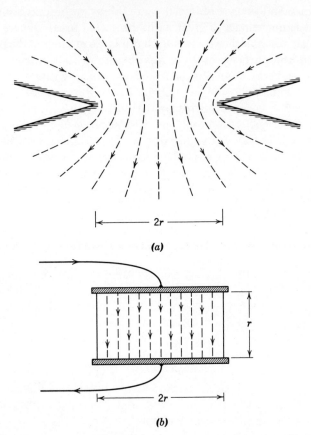

Fig. 3.11. (a) Real, (b) assumed appearance of a junction. It is assumed that all the electrical resistance is produced in the vicinity of the constriction.

πr^2 (Fig. 3.11) we find

$$R \approx \frac{\rho r}{\pi r^2} \approx \frac{\rho}{\pi r} \tag{3.8}$$

in good dimensional agreement with the correct eq. 3.7.

If we now have an interface with a large number of circular contacts, of radii $r_1 \ldots r_i \ldots r_N$, then we have for the total resistance R

$$\frac{1}{R} = \frac{1}{R_1} + \cdots \frac{1}{R_N}$$

$$= \frac{2\Sigma r_i}{\rho} \tag{3.9}$$

Equation 3.9 tells us something about the individual junctions, but by itself it is not enough to evaluate their size. If we assume all the junctions are of equal size, however, and if we also assume that eq. 3.2 may be applied, then we have

$$L = A_r \cdot p = n\pi r^2 p \qquad (3.10)$$

$$\frac{1}{R} = \frac{2nr}{\rho} \qquad (3.11)$$

$$\therefore r = \frac{2LR}{\pi p \rho}, \qquad n = \frac{\pi p \rho^2}{4LR^2} \qquad (3.12)$$

and the number and average size of the junctions may be separately estimated (Bowden and Tabor, 1954; Holm, 1958).

The results of calculations which have been carried out appear to be subject to severe systematic error because of the presence of two effects not considered in the simple theory.

1. The interaction which occurs when two junctions are close to each other. In this effect the same material must transmit current for both junctions; consequently the effective constriction resistance is increased above the value given in eq. 3.9 and hence the number of junctions computed from eq. 3.12 will be too small.

2. The presence of electrically resistant surface films. When these occur there is a component of electric resistance over and above the constriction effect.

Nevertheless, the electrical resistance method is considered an extremely important way of studying surfaces, since it may be used both for stationary and sliding surfaces, whereas many other methods can be applied to only one or the other category.

Temperature method.   We may estimate the size of the junctions by measuring the thermal resistance of a junction, quite analogous to the way that we have already considered electrical resistance measurements.   The difference in the two methods is that the presence of oxide films at the interface is less serious, since these films disturb the flow of heat much less severely than they do the flow of electricity.   On the other hand, substantial amounts of heat flow may occur through the air gap between the specimens, away from the junctions, and a correction must be applied for this effect.

If we are considering sliding specimens, we may measure the temperature produced in sliding to estimate the size of the junction.   The temperature rise produced during sliding varies inversely with r at low speeds of sliding (see eq. 4.14).   Newcomb (1957) has measured the temperature of sliding copper on constantan, and lead on steel surfaces, and, assuming eq. 3.2 to hold, has been able to calculate quite plausible values for the junction size.

Optical and sectioning methods. Optical methods use a transparent material as one of the contacting bodies. This allows direct observation of the number and size of the contacts. Thus Dyson and Hirst (1954) pressed a steel surface against a glass surface covered by a thin silver layer, and were able, by observation through the glass, to study the extent of the real area of contact. Apart from the fact that this method is restricted to transparent materials, and also to measurements of the initial stages of contact, before sliding has caused appreciable surface damage, it does provide much useful information.

A similar but more direct method is that of Kraghelsky and Demkin (1960), who used the fact that when a solid touches the surface of a transparent body it can interfere with the full internal reflection from that surface.

West (1953) and also Feng (1952) have taken sections perpendicular to the interface, and have thus been able to make direct observations of junctions. This technique is interesting, but very tedious.

Wear measurements and scratch measurements. The use of wear measurements to give information about the surface interaction is based on the premise that an intimate connection exists between the size of the junctions produced during sliding and the size of wear particles formed from those junctions. As a first approximation, it is assumed that the linear dimensions of the adhesive wear particles are the same as those of the junctions (Rabinowicz, 1953). All that remains, then, is to measure the size distribution of wear particles formed after normal contact or after sliding contact, and equate the wear particle size to the junction size. This provides an estimate of the size of the junctions that were present during contact (Fig. 3.12).

As we shall see in later chapters, wear measurements have been of great help in giving us an idea of the size of junctions and, generally, the *scale* of the friction process. But in practice they seem to be more applicable to sliding surfaces than to those which have undergone purely normal loading, because in the latter case thin contaminant films greatly affect (i.e., reduce) the size of the observed wear particles.

A method analogous to that of measuring wear particles but which appears to have been used only in a qualitative way consists of measuring the width of the scratches formed when one smooth material slides on another. It may reasonably be assumed that the width of the scratches corresponds to the width of the junctions, and, if a hard

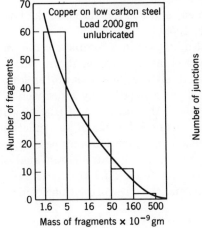
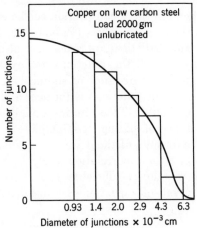

Fig. 3.12a. Measured size distribution of wear particles formed during sliding.
Fig. 3.12b. Size distribution of junctions, computed from data of Fig. 3.12a, assuming that fragments and junctions have the same diameter.

material is slid on a soft one, the number of scratches may be assumed to be equal to the number of junctions.

Statistical analysis of friction traces. This method is applicable only to sliding surfaces, but for systems of this kind it does constitute a very powerful tool for analyzing the sizes and number of the junctions formed. The assumptions underlying the method are that each junction formed has a shear stress that is likely to be different from the strength of other junctions, and that this strength is maintained during the life of the junction. As sliding continues, the friction will fluctuate as the junction population varies. Thus, at an instant when all the junctions happen to be strong the friction will be high, whereas at a later instant when the junctions are weak the friction will be low (Rabinowicz, Rightmire, Tedholm, and Williams, 1955).

If an assumption is made as to the range in strength between the weakest and strongest junctions, and a factor of 2 seems plausible in many cases, it is possible to estimate from the amplitude fluctuations how many junctions must have been present at any time. The actual expression for number of junction, assuming them all equal in size, takes the form

$$\frac{\sigma}{\bar{f}} = \frac{1}{4\sqrt{n}} \tag{3.13}$$

when $\bar{f}$ is the mean friction coefficient and σ is the standard deviation in the friction values (Rabinowicz, 1956).

The statistical approach may also be used in a completely different way.   If all the junctions at any instant are strong, it will take an appreciable distance of sliding before all the junctions are broken, a new set of junctions is formed, and the strength may be expected to drop again.   Thus, from an analysis of the variation of friction with distance of sliding, it is possible to deduce the size of the junctions. The formula of the diameter of the average junction may be obtained from an autocorrelation analysis.   In carrying out such an analysis, the friction coefficients $f_1 \ldots f_j \ldots f_k \ldots f_n$ are measured at intervals off a friction-distance plot, and the autocorrelation coefficient

$$r_k = \frac{n}{n-k} \frac{\Sigma_1^n (f_j - \bar{f})(f_{j+k} - \bar{f})}{\Sigma_1^n (f_j - \bar{f})^2} \tag{3.14}$$

is calculated (Rabinowicz, 1956).   The distance k at which the autocorrelation drops to zero is equal to twice the average junction diameter (Fig. 3.13).

One of the attractive features of the statistical method is that the number of junctions and the size of junctions are computed independ-

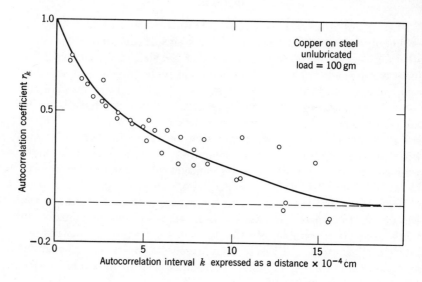

Fig. 3.13.   Autocorrelation coefficient of friction traces as a function of distance along the sliding track.   Since r_k drops to zero in 18×10^{-4} cm, the average junction diameter is 9×10^{-4} cm.

ently, and hence a check on the validity of both methods is possible, since the total area of contact must be close to the value given in eq. 3.2. The agreement in practice is encouragingly good.

It should also be mentioned that the autocorrelation method may be extended to deduce the size distribution of the junctions. This is done by using all the autocorrelation coefficients, not just the one at which the autocorrelation reaches zero (Rabinowicz, 1957). Again, agreement with the size-distribution deduced from wear particle measurements is quite good.

Finally we might point out that there is a close similarity between autocorrelation studies of friction traces, and studies of the initiation of sliding when a tangential load is first applied to an interface. Observations made in such studies, and analogous studies of systems which are borderline with respect to stick-slip, may be used to deduce the size of junctions (Rabinowicz, 1958).

3.6 The Size of Junctions

In the preceding section we have briefly described a number of ways in which the sizes and numbers of junctions may be estimated. In addition to these experimental methods, there is available to us a theoretical method of somewhat dubious validity, based on the fact that we would expect to find that the sizes of junctions are equal to the sizes of adherent fragments formed during sliding (Rabinowicz, 1964). The diameter d_A of adherent fragments, as is shown later in Section 6.17, is given by

$$d_A = 24,000 \, \frac{\gamma}{p} \qquad (3.15)$$

where γ and p represent the surface energy and hardness of the softer material respectively.

It should be emphasized that this estimate of junction diameter is a relatively poor one, in that it ignores completely the other, harder, surface, which clearly must influence the junction size. Nevertheless, the computed values of junction diameters based on eq. 3.15 are not out of line with those measured experimentally, as is shown in Table 3.1.

This table shows estimates of junction size for copper and steel surfaces, either clean or lightly contaminated, as determined by a number of different methods. Also included are computed values of junction size based on eq. 3.15. It will be seen that the general level of agreement is reasonably satisfactory, if we bear in mind the rudimentary state of the theory.

Table 3.1 Estimates of Junction Diameter

Combination	Load	Lubricant	Method	Junction Diameter	Reference
Copper on steel	1 kg	None	f_s — distance	7μ	Rabinowicz, 1951
Steel on copper	1 kg	None	f_s — distance	6μ	Rabinowicz, 1951
Copper on copper	1 kg	Cetane	f_s — distance	8μ	Rabinowicz, 1951
Copper on steel	2 kg	None	Particle size	31μ	Rabinowicz, 1953
Copper on copper	0.1 kg	None	f_k autocorrelation	10μ	Rabinowicz, 1956
Copper on copper	0.1 kg	None	f_k fluctuations	5μ	Rabinowicz, 1956
Steel on steel	50 kg	Contaminated	$f_s - t$ vs. $f_k - v$	10μ	Rabinowicz, 1958
Copper on copper	Any	None	$24000\ \gamma/p$	26μ	Eq. 3.15
Steel on steel	Any	None	$24000\ \gamma/p$	13μ	Eq. 3.15

References

Abrikosova, I. I., and B. V. Deryagin (1957), Direct Measurement of Molecular Attraction between Solids in Vacuum, *Soviet Physics JETP*, **4**, 2–10.

Bowden, F. P., and D. Tabor (1939), The Area of Contact between Stationary and between Moving Surfaces, *Proc. Roy. Soc.* A **169**, 391–402.

Bowden, F. P., and D. Tabor (1954), *The Friction and Lubrication of Solids, Pt. I*, Clarendon Press, Oxford, p. 31.

Courtney-Pratt, J. S., and E. Eisner (1957), The Effect of a Tangential Force on the Contact of Metallic Bodies, *Proc. Roy. Soc.*, A **238**, 529–550.

Dyson, J., and W. Hirst (1954), The True Contact Area between Solids, *Proc. Phys. Soc. (London)*, **67B**, 309–312.

Feng, I. M. (1952), Metal Transfer and Wear, *J. Appl. Phys.*, **23**, 1011–1019.

Halliday, J. S. (1957), Application of Reflection Electron Microscopy to the Study of Wear, pp. 647–651 of *Proc. Conf. Lubrication and Wear*, Institution of Mechanical Engineers, London.

Holm, R. (1958), *Electric Contacts Handbook*, Springer-Verlag, Berlin.

Kraghelsky, I. V., and N. B. Demkin (1960), Determination of the True Contact Area, published in *Friction and Wear in Machinery*, translated by the A.S.M.E., New York, **14**, 30–53.

Menter, J. W., and D. W. Pashley (1959), The Microstructure and Mechanical Properties of Thin Films, pp. 111–150 of *Structure and Properties of Thin*

Films, ed. by C. A. Neugebauer, J. B. Newkirk, and O. A. Vermilyea, Wiley, New York.

Moore, A. C., and D. Tabor (1952), Some Mechanical and Adhesive Properties of Indium, *Br. J. Appl. Phys.*, **3**, 299–301.

Newcomb, T. P. (1957), Communication on pp. 837–838 of *Proc. Conf. Lubrication and Wear*, Institution of Mechanical Engineers, London.

O'Connor, T. L., and H. H. Uhlig (1957), Absolute Areas of Some Metallic Surfaces, *J. Phys. Chem.*, **61**, 402–405.

Rabinowicz, E. (1951), The Nature of the Static and Kinetic Coefficients of Friction, *J. Appl. Phys.*, **22**, 1373–1379.

Rabinowicz, E. (1953), A Quantitative Study of the Wear Process, *Proc. Phys. Soc. (London)*, **66B**, 929–936.

Rabinowicz, E. (1956), Autocorrelation Analysis of the Sliding Process, *J. Appl. Phys.*, **27**, 131–135.

Rabinowicz, E. (1957), Investigation of Size Effects in Sliding by Means of Statistical Techniques, pp. 276–280 of *Proc. Conf. Lubrication and Wear*, Institution of Mechanical Engineers, London.

Rabinowicz, E. (1958), The Intrinsic Variables Affecting the Stick-Slip Process, *Proc. Phys. Soc. (London)*, **71**, 668–675.

Rabinowicz, E. (1961), Influence of Surface Energy on Friction and Wear Phenomina, *J. Appl. Phys.*, **32**, 1440–1444.

Rabinowicz, E. (1964), Practical Uses of the Surface Energy Criterion, *Wear*, **7**, 9–22.

Rabinowicz, E., B. G. Rightmire, C. E. Tedholm, and R. E. Williams (1955), The Statistical Nature of Friction, *Trans. Am. Soc. Mech. Eng.*, **77**, 981–984.

Tabor, D. (1951), *The Hardness of Metals*, Oxford University Press, Oxford.

Tolansky, S. (1953), "Specialized Microscopical Techniques in Metallurgy," pp. 1–22 of *Properties of Metallic Surfaces*, Institute of Metals, London.

West, A. C. (1953), Friction and Boundary Lubrication, *Lubrication Engineering*, **9**, 211–217.

4

Friction

4.1 Introduction

Friction is the resistance to motion which exists when a solid object is moved tangentially with respect to the surface of another which it touches, or when an attempt is made to produce such motion. The importance of friction may be seen in the fact that, as estimates show, a very substantial part of the total energy consumption of mankind is expended in overcoming frictional losses during sliding. Reduction of friction, either through improved design, or through the use of more suitable contacting materials, or again through the application of better lubricating substances, is thus an extremely important problem of modern technology.

It must not be overlooked, however, that very many processes of everyday life are dependent for their effectiveness on the presence of friction in large enough amounts. Hence the provision when required, of sufficiently large friction is also a task of great importance. We are all familiar with the fact that such simple processes as walking, or driving a car (in regard to starting, stopping, and cornering), or gripping objects in our hands, cannot be readily carried out if friction is too low. When this occurs, we say that conditions are "slippery," and it becomes a friction problem to find a remedy. The maintenance of sufficiently high friction is required also in the function of such common devices as nails, screws and other fasteners.

Although the foregoing two categories comprise the two main frictional requirements, that of lowering friction when unwanted or of maintaining it at a sufficiently high level when required, there is a third problem of some importance, that of maintaining friction constant within narrow limits. A typical example is provided by the brakes of an automobile, which will not stop the car rapidly enough if the friction is too low, but which will give passengers an unpleasant jerk forward if friction is too high. Other applications where friction must be under close control are in the metal-rolling industry, and also in precision devices of many kinds where accurately controllable motion is desired.

A fourth problem of considerable importance in many practical applications is that of curing friction-caused oscillations which manifest themselves as squeaks, squeals, and chattering sounds. The opposite requirement, namely that of providing conditions suitable for the occurrence of frictional oscillations, exists for instruments of the violin family, which produce sounds only by means of such oscillations.

4.2 Quantitative Laws of Sliding Friction

Friction is expressed in quantitative terms as a force, being the force exerted by either of two contacting bodies tending to oppose relative tangential displacement of the other. It is necessary to distinguish between two situations, namely that in which the applied force is insufficient to cause motion, and the other in which sliding is occurring.

As typical of the first case we may consider a weight L resting on a horizontal flat surface (Fig. 4.1). If a small tangential force P is applied it is found experimentally that sliding does not occur. It is clear in this case (through application of Newton's First Law) that the friction force at the interface must be exactly equal and opposite to P. If the tangential force is decreased, say to $P/2$, it is found experimentally that the friction force also decreases to $P/2$, again equal and opposite to the applied force. This illustrates the first qualitative property of the friction force: "In any situation where the resultant of the tangential forces is smaller than some force parameter specific to that particular situation, the friction force will be equal and opposite to the resultant of the applied forces and no tangential motion will occur."

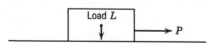

Fig. 4.1. Schematic illustration for a load on a horizontal surface. A tangential force P is applied.

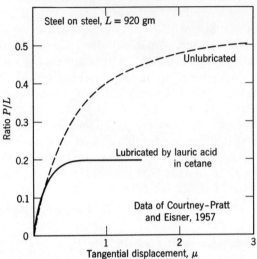

Fig. 4.2.   Plot of the P/L ratio required to produce tangential displacement of magnitude shown.

Exceptions to this law are found only on a microscopic scale. A number of workers, among whom we may mention Stevens (1899), Rankin (1926), and Courtney-Pratt and Eisner (1957) have shown that when the tangential force P is first applied, a very small displacement of the weight in the direction of P, through a distance of perhaps 10^{-5} or 10^{-4} cm, occurs almost instantaneously (Fig. 4.2). Thereafter motion stops, unless one of the materials has a tendency to creep. In that case the weight will tend to creep over the surface at initially reasonably small speeds (say 10^{-6} cm/sec), which subsequently become vanishingly small. With very soft materials such as indium and lead a slow steady sliding speed, in the $10^{-6} - 10^{-8}$ cm/sec range, however, is maintained for long periods of time (Ernst and Merchant, 1940; Burwell and Rabinowicz, 1953; c.f. Fig. 4.3). It is clear that, accompanying these phenomena, there must be very slight inequalities between the tangential force P and the friction force F.

The next situation to consider is that in which the applied force P is sufficient to cause sliding; that is, when P is applied, the weight moves. It is found experimentally that the body moves in the direction of P, and from this it follows that the friction force, although smaller than P, is still colinear with P. This may be considered the second qualitative property of the friction force: "When tangential motion occurs, the friction force always acts in a direction opposite to that of the relative velocity of the surfaces."

Exceptions to this law are also only minor in nature. It has been found that, for surfaces without pronounced directional properties, the instantaneous friction force may fluctuate by a degree or so from its assigned direction (Fig. 4.4), changing direction continuously and in random fashion as sliding proceeds (Rabinowicz, 1959). If the surface has lapping marks or other scratches in one direction, or is the face of a crystal, the friction force may vary from its assigned direction by a few degrees if relative motion is at an angle to the "grain" of the surface (Halaunbrenner, 1960).

The remaining laws of friction are concerned with the magnitude of the friction force. Three quantitative relations are required to express the magnitude of the friction force as a function of the principal

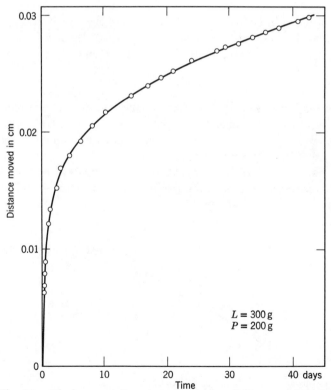

Fig. 4.3. Displacement-time curve for steel on indium, unlubricated.

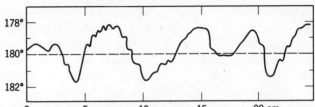

Fig. 4.4. Direction of the friction force as measured from the sliding direction. Steel on steel, lubricated by a machine oil. Load 1000 gm, velocity 5 cm/sec.

macroscopically observable variables, namely the applied load, the size of the region of contact, and the sliding velocity. The three quantitative relations are as follows:

1. The friction force F is proportional to the normal force L, that is,

$$F = fL \qquad (4.1)$$

This relationship enables us to define a coefficient of friction f (or μ). Alternatively, it is often convenient to express this law in terms of a constant angle of repose, or frictional angle θ defined by

$$\tan \theta = f \qquad (4.2)$$

It may readily be shown that θ is the angle of an inclined plane such that any object, whatever its weight, placed on the plane will remain stationary, but that, if the angle is increased by any amount whatever, the object will slide down (Fig. 4.5).

2. The friction force is independent of the apparent area of contact A_a. Thus large and small objects have the same coefficients of friction.

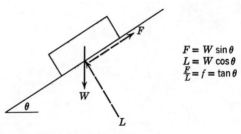

$$F = W \sin \theta$$
$$L = W \cos \theta$$
$$\frac{F}{L} = f = \tan \theta$$

Fig. 4.5. Equilibrium diagram for an object on an inclined plane. Slippage down the plane is impending.

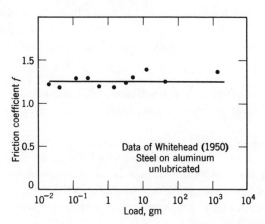

Fig. 4.6. For steel on aluminum, the friction is independent of load over a wide range of loads.

3. The friction force is independent of the sliding velocity v. This implies that the force required to initiate sliding will be the same as the force to maintain sliding at any specified velocity.

Taken together, these three laws provide the quantitative framework within which friction is generally considered by engineers. It is therefore important to discover how closely these laws apply in actual practice.

The first two quantitative laws are generally well obeyed, to within a few per cent in most cases (Figs. 4.6, 4.7). Exceptions to the first of

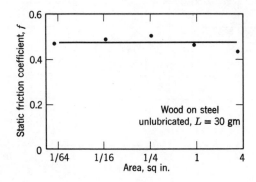

Fig. 4.7. The effect of changes in contact area on the friction of wood on steel. No significant variation is found.

them occur mostly with very hard materials like diamond or very soft materials like Teflon (Fig. 4.8). In many cases, sliding combinations involving materials such as they obey a law of the kind

$$F = c \cdot L^x \qquad (4.3)$$

where c is a constant and x a fraction varying somewhere in the range from $\frac{2}{3}$ to 1. Naturally, in cases where the first law is obeyed, x is exactly 1.

Another case where the friction force is not proportional to the load involves a surface with a thin hard surface layer and a softer substrate. At low loads the hard thin surface layer remains unbroken and its friction properties predominate. At high loads the surface layer is broken through and the properties of the substrate become the more important (Fig. 4.9).

Deviations from the second quantitative law, which states that friction is independent of the apparent area of contact, are sometimes noted in very smooth and very clean surfaces. Under these conditions

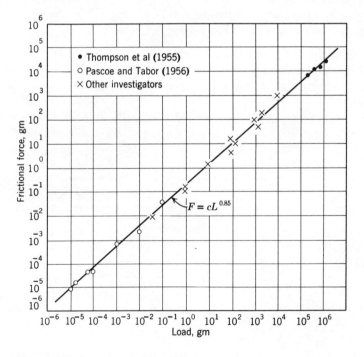

Fig. 4.8. Data collected by Allan (1958) on the effect of load on the friction of Teflon.

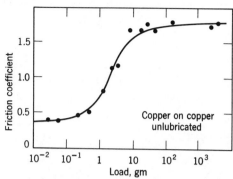

Fig. 4.9.   Data of Whitehead (1950) on the variation of the friction of copper with the applied load.

very strong interaction between the surfaces takes place, so that the friction force becomes independent of the load but proportional merely to the apparent area of contact (which has become the real area of contact).   Such cases are discussed later.

It should be emphasized that the first and second quantitative laws are generally well obeyed, and that exceptions to them are rarities. Far different is the position of the third law which states that friction is independent of velocity.   It is well known that the friction force required to start sliding is usually greater than the force required to maintain sliding, and this has given rise to the notion that there are two coefficients of friction—static (for surfaces at rest) and kinetic (for surfaces in motion).   These are normally shown separately in tables of friction coefficients.

Recent work has shown, however, that this is a gross oversimplification, and that the static friction coefficient is a function of time of contact (Dokos, 1946), whereas the kinetic friction coefficient is a function of velocity throughout the range of velocities.   A schematic representation of typical static friction-time and kinetic friction-velocity plots is shown in Figs. 4.10 and 4.11.

It should be noted that the static friction coefficient varies most markedly at short times of static contact (say below 0.1 sec), whereas at longer times of contact the friction coefficient is a logarithmic function of the time of stick, increasing by a few per cent only for every tenfold increase in time of static contact.

The kinetic friction coefficient generally has a positive slope at slow sliding speeds and a negative slope at high sliding speeds.   These

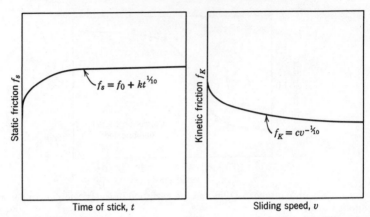

Fig. 4.10. Typical plot of static coefficient as a function of time of stick (Rabinowicz, 1957).
Fig. 4.11. Typical plot of kinetic coefficient as a function of sliding speed (Barwell, 1956).

slopes tend to be straight lines over wide ranges of velocity when the friction coefficient is plotted as a function of log velocity (Fig. 4.12). Usually the slopes are fairly small, that is, the friction coefficients change by just a few per cent as the sliding speed is raised by a factor of 10. In consequence of the combined positive and negative, but gentle, slopes of the typical friction-velocity curve, it is found that over

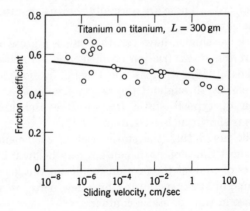

Fig. 4.12. Friction-velocity curve of hard materials has slightly negative slope over wide range.

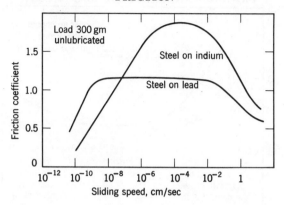

Fig. 4.13. Friction-velocity curve of materials which creep has positive slope at low speeds, negative slope at high speeds.

a speed range of as much as a factor of 10^{10} the friction coefficient hardly varies by as much as a factor of 2 (Fig. 4.13). For many purposes in which only limited velocity ranges are of interest the kinetic friction coefficients may be taken to be a constant independent of the sliding velocity.

Of special interest are sliding systems in which the coefficient of friction decreases as the velocity increases. Within this velocity range, friction oscillations may arise, and thus the squeaking and chattering of many sliding systems is produced. This phenomenon is explored in section 4-15.

The reader will have noted that no mention has been made, in the foregoing discussion, of the surface roughness. Perhaps we might produce a law specifically to apply to the case of surface roughness "The friction force is independent of the roughness of the sliding surfaces."

Actually, this rule is somewhat of an oversimplification. A complete plot of friction as a function of surface roughness, over a very wide range of surface roughnesses, would look as shown in Fig. 4.14. With very smooth surfaces, the friction tends to be high because the real area of contact grows excessively, whereas with very rough surfaces the friction is high because of the need to lift one surface over the asperities on the other. In the intermediate range of roughness, that normally used in engineering practice, the friction is at a minimum and almost independent of roughness.

An exceptional situation, in which a rough surface gives higher friction than a smoother one, is that in which a rough hard body slides on a much softer one. Here the asperities of the rough surface enable it

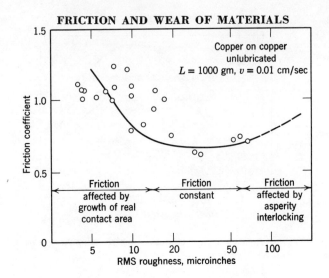

Fig. 4.14. Plot of friction against roughness shows a negative slope region caused by excessive junction growth, and a positive region caused by the interlocking of asperities. In between, friction is independent of roughness.

to dig into the softer material, and, when sliding occurs, we must shear a much larger area of the soft surface than is represented by A_r.

Now that we have examined the experimental laws of friction, we shall attempt to deduce a theoretical model of friction, and see how well we can explain the experimental results.

4.3   The Origin and Magnitude of the Friction Force

In Chapter 3 we derived eq. 3.2 for the real area of contact which exists when two materials are pressed together.   This calculation will now be extended by considering the case where the surfaces are pressed together by a load L and sliding is induced by a friction force F.   If we assume that, when sliding occurs the average shear stress over the real area of contact has the value of τ_{Av}, we can write an equation for the total friction force F in the form

$$F = \tau_{Av} \cdot A_r \qquad (4.4)$$

Whence the coefficient of friction

$$f = \frac{F}{L} = \frac{\tau_{Av} \cdot A_r}{p \cdot A_r} = \frac{\tau_{Av}}{p} \qquad (4.5)$$

It remains to evaluate the average resistance to shear of the junctions constituting the real area of contact. By using a limit analysis, it is easy to show that this shear strength cannot substantially exceed the bulk shear strength τ_y, hereafter referred to as s, of the softer of the contacting materials. If it did, each junction would shear within the softer material as soon as a shear force was applied sufficient to produce shear stresses of this magnitude. This would produce a particle of the weaker material adhering to the surface of the harder material (Fig. 4.15). In fact, the rate of production of such particles is about 1–10% of the rate of formation and break up of junctions, when uncontaminated metals slide together in an air environment (c.f. Table 6.1), and from this we deduce that most junctions are about as strong as, or nearly as strong as, the weaker contacting material. Hence we may write

$$F = s \cdot A_r$$

$$\therefore f = \frac{s}{p} \tag{4.6}$$

In eq. 4.6 the friction coefficient f is written as the ratio of two quantities s and p, representing respectively the resistance to plastic flow of the weaker of the contacting materials in shear and in compression. Since these are very similar quantities, depending in almost the same way on such properties of the materials as bond strength, nature of dislocations, etc., it is not surprising to find that the ratio is quite similar for a wide range of materials. Thus, materials like lead and low carbon steel vary by nearly a factor of 100 in shear strength and penetration hardness, but f, representing the ratio of these two quantities, is nearly the same for steel (1.0) as it is for lead (1.2).

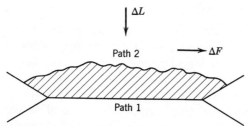

Fig. 4.15. A junction being sheared. If the shear strength of the junction is much bigger than the bulk strength of the top material, shear will take place along path 2, producing the fragment shaded.

The preceding formulation neatly explains the observed laws of friction.

1. The existence of static frictional strength of interfaces, namely the fact that a certain minimum tangential force is required to produce motion, is typical of plastic deformations in general (cf. Fig. 2.2). Any slight motion observed at lower values of the applied shear force is readily explained in terms of elastic and creep deformations of the individual contact regions.

2. The fact that the force resisting the movement is in the direction opposite to that of the displacement is another characteristic behavior of isotropic materials deformed plastically. Only in special cases where the contacts are anisotropic, does departure from this general rule become pronounced.

3. The proportionality of friction force and applied load is a direct consequence of the fact that each is equal to a material constant, characteristic of the surfaces in contact, multiplied by the same real area of contact A_r.

4. The independence of the friction force relative to the apparent area of contact A_a is readily explained in terms of the concept that it is the real area, rather than the apparent area, which governs the interaction between the two materials. This real area of contact is not dependent on the apparent area.

5. The weak dependence of the friction force on the sliding velocity may be explained as part of a more general phenomenon, namely the small dependence of the strengths of most solids on the rate of application of the stress. Solids which have a pronounced dependence of strength on strain rate generally show a pronounced dependence of friction force on sliding velocity.

6. The weak dependence of friction on surface roughness is to be expected, since little frictional work is done in overcoming surface roughness, most of the work being done in inducing shear displacement of the junction interface.

A number of other frictional phenomena are readily explained by the foregoing postulated friction mechanism. First, there is the role of lubricants, which form thin layers of low shear strength between the contacting materials, thus producing a system with low shear strength s, but high flow pressure p, and hence low friction. Along the same lines, the drop in friction universally observed as sliding speeds are raised to very high values is a consequence of the thermal softening of the interface, so that s becomes low, whereas the substrate is cooler and hence has suffered less softening (p high).

4.4 Criticisms of the Adhesion Theory

From time to time a number of criticisms have been put forward of the model presented earlier, which constitutes the adhesion theory of friction. Although the adhesional theory is at present supported by a goodly majority of workers in the friction field it is worthwhile discussing those criticisms of the theory in some detail, especially since the acceptance of the theory is still confined largely to these workers. The main criticisms of the adhesional theory have centered on the following points.

1. The theory states that friction is independent of roughness, but this is opposed to common sense and to experience. Common sense or not, however it is a fact that although grossly rough surfaces do show high friction (because of the need during sliding to lift one surface over the humps on the other), very smooth surfaces show even higher friction, because of the increase in the real area of contact (Fig. 4.14).

2. It is not readily apparent how the strong junctions between the contacting materials, as strong as actual welds, are produced, bearing in mind that, in many cases, the temperature at the contacts is quite low, that interdiffusion of the surface atoms is unlikely to occur, and that the alignment of the surface atoms is likely to be poor. This objection has lost much of its force as a consequence of recent work in adhesion (Chapter 9), which has shown that clean metals (e.g., aluminum) adhere very strongly when pressed together in such a way as to extend and break up oxide and other surface films.

3. A more important criticism is that, although strong adhesion between the contacting materials is postulated in the theory, it is a fact that if the normal force pressing the surfaces together is removed, this adhesion cannot be detected. This point is also dealt with in Chapter 9, which shows that the junctions are deformed elastically as well as plastically, and that removal of the load breaks off most of the junctions, as result of elastic springback.

4. Fourth, objection is made on the ground that the brittle nonmetals, with which plastic deformation does not occur, do show frictional properties similar to those of the metals. This point loses validity, however, when we realize that the material at the interface is under high compressive stress, and that brittle materials do deform plastically under these high compressive stresses.

5. Finally, there are objections based on the magnitude of the friction force. It is known that for most materials the shear strength s is about $\frac{1}{2}$ of σ_y, the plastic yield strength in tension, and the penetration

hardness p is about $3\sigma_y$ (see Section 2.4).   Hence, the ratio s/p has a value of about $\frac{1}{6}$, whereas actual friction values, which according to eq. 4.6 should equal s/p, are about 0.4, or about two or three times as great as s/p.

Furthermore, the adhesion theory treats the normal stress p and the shear stress s as independent variables.   Yet in fact they are related by some yield criterion, so that when a high normal stress p is applied to an interface, the shear stress required to initiate sliding must be diminished.   Accordingly the derivation of eq. 4.6 is in error, and we should in practice expect friction coefficients smaller than s/p.

Also, we would expect friction phenomena to be affected by contaminants at the interface, so that experiments carried out in air would agree but poorly with eq. 4.6, but the agreement would become progressively better when the contaminants were removed by carrying out tests in dry air, then in vacuum, then, after outgassing at elevated temperatures, in a high vacuum.   In fact, tests carried out with clean metal surfaces in a good vacuum (e.g., copper) do not agree at all well with eq. 4.6, and the friction is found to be very high (order of magnitude 100) and depends critically on the surface geometry (Bowden and Hughes, 1939; Gwathmey, 1951; Bowden and Young, 1951).

These three problems are all resolved in the same way, namely that, as we saw in Fig. 3.4, the real area of contact tends to be larger than the value L/p which is assigned to it in eq. 3.2.   Since the actual value of A_r, once displacement starts, is larger than it "should" be by a factor of two or three, the shear strength has a substantial value, and the friction coefficient is correspondingly larger than the "theoretical" value of $\frac{1}{6}$.   The very high values of friction coefficient observed with very clean metals are due to a further increase in A_r, above the value just considered, because of the coming into play of surface energy effects.   If we combine eq. 3.6 with an expression for the shear force at a circular junction of radius r, namely

$$\Delta F = s \cdot \pi r^2 \tag{4.7}$$

we find

$$\frac{\Delta F}{\Delta L} = \frac{s}{p} \cdot \frac{1}{1 - 2W_{ab}\cot\theta/rp} \tag{4.8}$$

Equation 4.8 becomes the relation for the friction coefficient, if we regard θ as an average surface roughness angle, and r as an average junction radius.   We see that very high values of friction coefficient can occur when the ratio of surface energy of adhesion W_{ab} to hardness p is high, and the surface roughness angle θ is very small.   These are

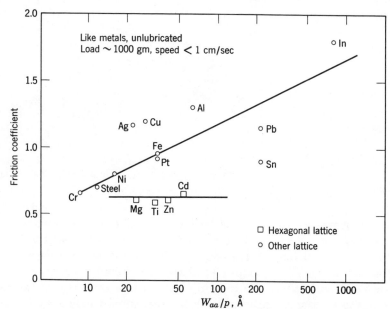

Fig. 4.16. Friction coefficients for clean like metals. Except with hexagonal latticed metals, the friction coefficient and the W_{aa}/p ratio increase together.

indeed the conditions which produce very high friction coefficients (Figs. 4.14 and 4.16).

At this point we may leave our discussion of the adhesion theory of friction (eq. 4.6), and move on to a description of subsidiary contributions to the friction force. Although we feel that this theory is essentially correct, it does present, as we have seen, a grossly oversimplified picture of the friction process. In spite of these limitations, the theory has proved so useful in practice that most workers in the friction field would rather amend it than abandon it.

4.5 Other Contributions to the Friction Force

We have shown that the main resistance to sliding arises from the need to shear strongly adherent surface atoms of the contacting materials. Although this nearly always accounts for 90% or more of the overall friction force, there are a number of other factors to be taken into account.

1. *The roughness component.* This arises from the need, during the sliding of rough surfaces, to lift one surface over the roughnesses of the other. If the asperity has an inclination of θ, a contribution to the

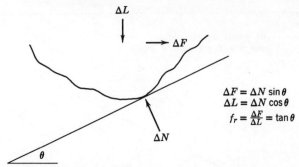

$$\Delta F = \Delta N \sin \theta$$
$$\Delta L = \Delta N \cos \theta$$
$$f_r = \frac{\Delta F}{\Delta L} = \tan \theta$$

Fig. 4.17. Free body diagram for an asperity sliding up a frictionless incline. The roughness component of friction f_r is equal to tan θ.

friction coefficient of tan θ will be produced (Fig. 4.17). At a later time, however, there may be a negative roughness component of friction, since θ will tend to take on negative as well as positive values (Fig. 4.18). Summing up for all the contacts, we note that regions of positive θ and negative θ coexist, so that to some extent the roughness friction terms tend to cancel out. What remains is usually a contribution of about 0.05 to the overall friction coefficient (Strang and Lewis, 1950), representing a fluctuating force superposed on the main adhesive component of the friction force.

An apparent exception to this rule that roughness has little effect on friction sometimes prevails for surfaces lubricated by liquids. At certain velocities, the smooth surfaces may be functioning in a state of hydrodynamic lubrication (f very low), while the rough surfaces are boundary lubricated (f much higher, Fig. 4.19). It is this factor, for example which makes automobile tires with treads better than smooth tires on a wet road. This has no relevance to the problem of dry sliding, however.

2. *The plowing component.* If a hard surface with sharp end is slid over a soft surface, it will tend to dig into the softer surface during sliding and produce a groove. The energy of deformation represented by the groove must be supplied by the friction force, which will therefore be larger than if no such groove had been produced.

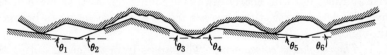

Fig. 4.18. Schematic illustration of two rough sliding surfaces. Many of the junctions are "sliding downhill."

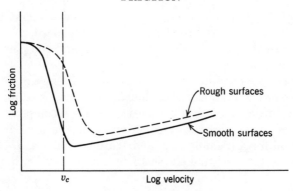

Fig. 4.19. Friction as a function of velocity for sliding surfaces. At velocities near v_c, the smooth surfaces are full fluid lubricated, whereas the rough surfaces are, to a large extent, boundary lubricated.

Similarly, sharp asperities on a hard surface can produce scratches when slid over a softer surface, and again an addition to the friction force is involved.

We may do a simple calculation for a circular cone of roughness angle θ (Fig. 4.20) pressed into a softer surface. During sliding, the penetrated area A_p swept out is given by

$$A_p = \tfrac{1}{2} \cdot 2r \cdot r \tan \theta = r^2 \tan \theta \tag{4.9}$$

If the additional resistance to sliding, consisting of the need to displace this area during sliding, is assumed equal to $A_p p$, we have

$$F = \pi r^2 s + r^2 \tan \theta \cdot p \tag{4.10}$$

$$L = \pi r^2 p$$

$$f = \frac{F}{L} = \frac{s}{p} + \frac{\tan \theta}{\pi} \tag{4.11}$$

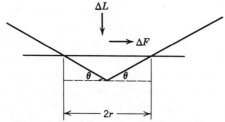

Fig. 4.20. Schematic illustration of a cone pressed into a flat surface. During sliding, a groove is swept out of projected area $r^2 \tan \theta$.

For really rough surfaces (e.g., sandpaper), tan θ might be 0.2 or larger and the plowing term is large (Avient, Goddard, and Wilman, 1960). Ordinarily, tan θ is about 0.05 or less, and the plowing term becomes negligible.

3. *Electrical components.* When unlike materials are placed in contact, it is known that an electrical double-layer may exist at the junctions. The breaking of the junctions must be accompanied by the separation of unlike electrical charges and hence lead to an increase in the friction force (Schnurmann and Wardlow-Davies, 1942). This effect appears to be extremely small in comparison with the other factors.

4.6   Friction of Metals

In the preceding sections we have described the *causes* of friction. We now turn to the frictional *effects* which are observed with materials, and we will first evaluate the frictional properties of metals, since metals are the most prominent constituents of today's machines and therefore are present in the vast majority of the sliding contacts in these machines. In most practical applications, sliding metal contacts are operated in the presence of lubricating substances such as oils, greases, or solid film lubricants, and the properties of lubricated surfaces are discussed in Chapter 8. In this chapter we shall be concerned with the situation, which arises quite frequently, in which the provision of a lubricant is impractical or impossible, or fails through some accident, or else the lubricant is heated above its effective working temperature, and then the metals are in contact under essentially dry conditions.

Before discussing the frictional properties of unlubricated metals in detail, it must be pointed out that these properties will be greatly affected by the presence of surface films on the metals, and that, in general, an unlubricated metal encountered in an industrial environment will be covered by a whole series of such films, as shown in Fig. 4.21. Working outward from the metal interior, we first encounter an oxide layer, produced by reaction of oxygen from the air with the metal, and present with all metals except the noble metals such as gold (see Section 2.5). Next will come an adsorbed layer derived from the atmosphere, the main constituents of this layer being generally molecules of water vapor and of oxygen (see Section 2.6). Outmost, these will usually be greasy or oil films.

Metal surfaces of this type generally have initial friction coefficients in the range 0.1 to 0.3 when slid together. Higher values are reached,

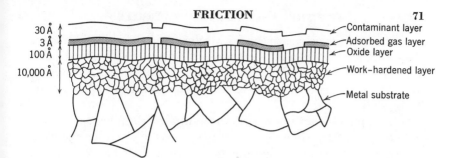

Fig. 4.21.   Schematic illustration of films on a metal surface (not to scale).

however, if the surfaces continue to be slid over each other, since under these conditions, the grease film, which is the one with the most drastic influence on the friction, will eventually be worn off.

4.7   Frictional Properties of Uncontaminated Metals in Air

Before describing the friction of clean metal surfaces we will do well to consider how such surfaces may be produced.

It is widely believed that, if it is unwanted, a grease film may be removed from a metal surface with a good solvent such as acetone or carbon tetrachloride. This is emphatically not so. Although the outer layers of the grease film dissolve readily in the solvent, the last layer, of thickness about 30Å or 10^{-7} in., is so tenaciously held to the metal that it will not go into solution unless the solvent is itself completely free of all grease-type material. In practice, the tendency is all the other way, and, if a perfectly grease-free metal surface is washed in a good solvent of commercial purity grade the metal surface itself will pick up contaminants from the solvent, of monolayer thickness, because of the high affinity that greasy substances have for clean metal surfaces.

To prepare grease-free metal surfaces, two main methods are available. Method A consists of preparing a new surface by a cutting process, either by abrading the surface with clean abrasive paper and/or lapping or polishing it under water, or alternatively by cutting it with a clean tool in the absence of a cutting fluid. Method B consists of dissolving the grease film from a previously prepared surface, either by treatment with a strong caustic soda solution, followed by rinsing in distilled water, or by allowing vapor from a pure organic solvent to condense on the surface and then to run off, carrying impurities with it. Some workers in the friction field prefer to follow up an abrasion-type treatment by a solvent purification. A surface which is relatively clean but does contain a trace of contaminant may be cleaned further by sliding it against a similar surface. The contaminant is gradually removed in association with wear debris formed during sliding.

Two simple tests are often used to confirm the cleanliness of a metal surface (Fig. 4.22). In one test a drop of water is placed on the metal surface; this will spread uniformly on a clean surface, but form a well-defined globule on a contaminated surface. The second test consists of breathing gently on the surface, thus condensing moisture on it. If the moisture is formed as a mist, rather than as a uniform and invisible film, the surface is contaminated. Both these tests depend on the same fact, namely, that water does not wet a grease film, but does wet a clean metal surface.

When two grease-free metal surfaces are slid together, the type of friction encountered varies with the nature of the contacting metals, and to a lesser extent with the other variables, namely load, surface area, surface roughness, and velocity. As a general rule it is found that two types of behavior are common. Following Archard and Hirst (1956), we may denote them respectively as severe frictional behavior and mild frictional behavior, and describe typical manifestations of each. Note that in some circumstances, the frictional behavior vascillates continuously between them.

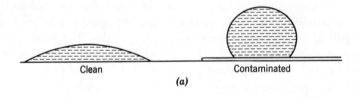

Clean   Contaminated

(a)

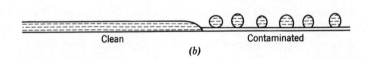

Clean   Contaminated

(b)

Fig. 4.22. (*a*) Appearance of a water drop on a metal surface. If the surface is clean, the drop continues to spread. (*b*) Metal surface after it is breathed on. If the moisture drops are visible, surface is contaminated.

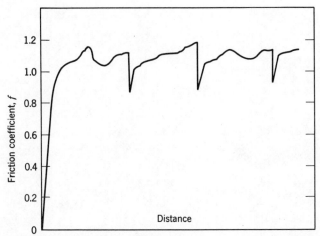

Fig. 4.23. Typical friction trace obtained with surfaces giving severe frictional behavior.

Severe frictional behavior. The friction coefficient is high (usually in the range 2.0 to 0.9). If a friction-detecting device with a good high-speed response is used, it will be found that there are large irregular fluctuations in the instantaneous values of the friction force (Fig. 4.23). Inspection of the surfaces after sliding will show but a few tracks where prominent points on one surface plowed through the other (Fig. 4.24), but these tracks will be large, and usually with irregular-appearing sides. Inspection in a microscope will disclose large particles (diameter exceeding 50 μ) transferred from one surface to the other.

Mild frictional behavior. The friction coefficient is lower (usually in the range 0.7 to 0.3). The friction coefficient is either very steady or else of the regular "stick-slip" type, in which the frictional force fluctuates in a regular manner between two well-defined extreme positions (Fig. 4.25). Inspection of the surfaces will disclose a large number of fine lines where small protuberances of one surface have ploughed a track through the other (Fig. 4.26). Small particles (diameter generally below 25 μ) will be found transferred from one surface to the other.

As a general rule, it is found that severe frictional behavior is found when the two sliding surfaces consist of the same metal, or when they consist of closely similar metals, as shown by the ability of the two

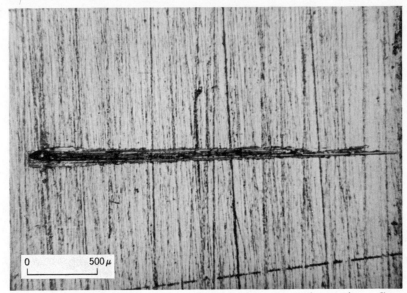

Fig. 4.24. Typical friction track produced during a severe interaction. Copper surface, after a steel flat has slid on it (the track was produced by a copper particle adhering to the steel.) x40.

metals to form alloys, or by the substantial solubility of atoms of one of the metals in a lattice of the other (Ernst and Merchant, 1940; Roach, Goodzeit, and Hunnicutt, 1956). Copper on copper (for example) gives high friction of above 1.0, because the same metal is used for both sliding surfaces, whereas aluminum, either on iron or on

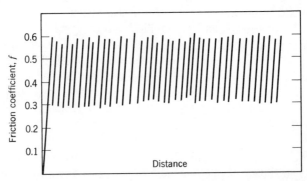

Fig. 4.25. Typical friction trace showing mild frictional behavior (stick-slip).

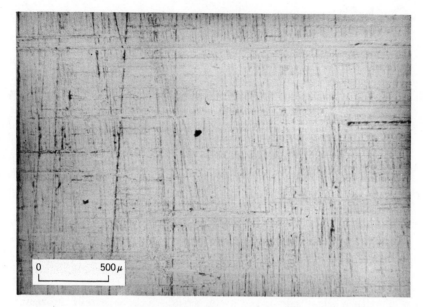

0   500 μ

Fig. 4.26. Typical friction track produced during a mild interaction. Same copper surface as Fig. 4.24, but showing tracks produced by steel particles. (The system copper-steel is borderline with respect to mild or severe frictional behavior).

low-carbon steel, gives high friction values of 0.8 and above (Goodzeit, Hunnicutt, and Roach, 1956) because these two metals interact strongly and form a whole host of intermetallic compounds (Hanson, 1958). Both systems cause severe surface damage.

Where the metals are unlike and of low affinity, mild sliding conditions as a rule prevail. Thus silver gives friction values of only about 0.3 on iron or on low-carbon steel, because these two metals do not alloy and form no compounds. In fact, molten silver and molten iron are immiscible (Hanson, 1958) and this I have found to be a good indication of incompatibility.

It should be made clear that the criterion of compatibility does not imply that the surface atoms of the two materials actually interdiffuse into each others' lattices; indeed, the low temperature rise and short contact times which characterize many sliding situations do not allow of any appreciable amounts of diffusion. Rather, we should note that the criteria for determining when the frictional behavior is mild or severe bear a very close relationship to the criteria of eq. 2.13, which determine whether W_{ab} is small or large (Machlin and Yankee, 1954). This naturally suggests that eq. 4.8, which gives the value of friction coefficient in terms of the ratio W_{ab}/p, may determine the occurrence of severe frictional behavior.

Although a quantitative test of eq. 4.8 has not yet been attempted, it is certainly true that eq. 4.8 gives a good qualitative indication of whether the frictional behavior will be mild or severe. First, we note that severe sliding conditions are the rule when one of the sliding metals is very soft (e.g. lead or indium) irrespective of the nature of the other. This is because the soft metal always gives a high W_{ab}/p ratio. As to mechanism, it is found that the soft metal readily coats the other metal with a film of its own fragments, whereupon the sliding system becomes for all practical purposes the soft metal sliding upon itself. Besides the very soft metals, a few harder metals, for example titanium and zirconium, show the same effect (Rabinowicz, 1954).

Second, we note that hard metals like iron, chromium, and nickel do not always show severe sliding behavior, even when slid against themselves, because they are characterized by low W_{ab}/p ratios. This trend is particularly marked when the harder metals are slid in a high-humidity atmosphere (Daniels and West, 1955), in which case the film of moisture adsorbed on the metal surface acts as a mild lubricant. With the soft metals, severe sliding conditions exist in both wet and dry atmospheres. The reduction of friction brought about by increased hardness is indicated in Fig. 4.16.

Third, there are questions of the mechanics of sliding, involving the surface geometry and the load. The effects of these variables can best be interpreted if we regard severe frictional behavior as a type of instability, brought on by the excessive growth and spreading into each other of the individual junctions. Thus, rough surfaces are not likely to give very high friction values (c.f. Fig. 4.14), because it is difficult for the junctions to grow to any marked degree. This is especially so when the lapping grooves, which constitute the surface roughness features, are at right angles to the sliding direction. Of course a reduced friction with increased surface roughness follows directly from eq. 4.8.

It is generally found that with material combinations like copper on low-carbon steel, which are marginal with respect to severe or mild frictional behavior, severe frictional behavior is much more likely when contact is constricted (i.e., the ratio of real to apparent area of contact, A_r/A_a, is high) than when it is not. When the junctions are close together, they can more readily grow into each other during sliding. Also, adherent wear particles, when they are close together, can cause the transfer of more particles by cooperative action (Rabinowicz, 1956).

For some metal combinations there is a minimum load such that severe sliding conditions are not encountered when the normal load during sliding is less than this minimum figure (Fig. 4.9). It has been shown that this minimum load often arises from the need to break through an oxide surface layer, thus enabling at least some metal-to-metal contact to be made in the system. This minimum load depends to some extent on the metals and the nature of the oxide film, as well as on the geometry of the contact and the surface finish of the metals.

As a special case within the foregoing classification, we must consider the sliding of metal alloys. Here it is necessary to distinguish between one-phase and multiphase alloys. The one-phase alloys (e.g., coin silver) behave like pure metals, generally having frictional properties similar to those of their major constituent. Sliding on themselves they generally give high friction and surface damage. The multiphase alloys (e.g., copper-lead bearing alloys) tend to behave quite differently, and often give mild frictional behavior; especially good sliding conditions are observed when the less prominent phase is softer than the other. In that case, the softer phase can get smeared out over the surface of the alloy, and can act as a lubricant, thus reducing friction and surface damage. Among alloy systems of this kind we may note the lead-containing free machining steels, and the graphite-containing cast irons.

The foregoing discussion of the friction of unlubricated metals has been based on the general assumption that it is the physical and mechanical properties of these metals which primarily determine their frictional behavior. The reader is warned that this is by no means a unanimously held view. Thus, Bowden and Tabor (1954, Chapter VII; 1964, Chapter III) lay great stress on the properties of oxide films at the interface, arguing that these films reduce the friction and wear and that the mechanical properties (e.g., hardness) of these oxides are of primary importance.

Although it is true that the properties of oxides have considerable influence on the overall frictional characteristics of a pair of metals (e.g., the friction for lead on lead as shown on Fig. 4.16 is lower than it "should" be, because PbO has some lubricating ability), the interaction of the two metals is of even greater importance, certainly at reasonably high loads. Also, the friction of noble metals (which form no oxides) is not out of line compared to other metals with the same γ/p ratio. Finally, it is not even universally true that oxides reduce the strength of the interaction between metals, for as Coffin (1956) has shown, some metal pairs have less friction and wear in an oxygen-free environment than they do in air.

4.8   Frictional Properties of Outgassed Metal Surfaces

In the previous section we considered metal surfaces which were exposed to the air, and thus had on their surfaces an adsorbed layer besides, in most cases, an oxide layer derived from the atmosphere.

It is possible to produce metal surfaces free of surface films, by working in a high-vacuum system (with a vacuum better than 10^{-7} mm of mercury) and by producing a new metal surface, either by machining off the surface layer initially present, or by evaporating or chemically reducing the initial layer at high temperature.

When two clean metal surfaces, prepared in this way, are slid together in the high vacuum, it is found that they have very high friction coefficients, values from 5 to 200 being quite common, and that, if sliding continues, there is a high degree of surface damage, the original surfaces being completely destroyed.   It is often found that after sliding for a small distance the surfaces adhere completely to each other, and a normal tensile force must be applied to separate them. A system consisting of two clean metals in a vacuum does not follow the normal laws of friction, since the friction force is almost independent of the applied load, but rather proportional to the area of contact, which grows inordinately during continued sliding.   In fact, the surfaces behave as if they had been welded together, and indeed the process they have undergone would be a satisfactory way of producing strong welds.

It is found that the very hard metals, for example, nickel, chromium, do not interact quite as strongly in the outgassed conditions as do softer ones, and friction coefficients of 2 to 3, without the accompaniment of gross welding, are the rule.

These frictional properties of metals in high vacua are an extreme example of severe frictional behavior, which may be attributed to the extremely high W_{ab} values of outgassed metal surfaces.

4.9   Friction of Non-metals

With respect to their frictional properties, non-metals show marked differences from the metals, which were considered in Sections 4.6 to 4.8.   These differences arise, basically, from the fact that metals have surfaces which, when naked, have high reactivities with the oxygen and water vapor in the air, and also have high surface energies, so that gases and grease films alike tend to be strongly adsorbed on them. Consequently, wide variations in the frictional properties of metals are found, depending on the exact degree of cleanliness of the surfaces, and it is important to know whether the metals are covered by a grease film, or by an oxide film, or by no film of any kind.

On the other hand, the occurrence of contamination in non-metals is less important. The question of oxide formation does not arise in most cases, and adsorbed films of various kinds, while under some conditions having a significant effect on the frictional properties, do not generally alter the frictional properties of non-metals as profoundly as they do those of metal surfaces.

A factor which must be borne in mind in considering the frictional properties of non-metals is that, in contrast with the metals which form a fairly homogeneous class, non-metals vary much more widely among themselves, including as they do such widely dissimilar substances, all of frictional importance, as diamond, rubber, concrete, leather, nylon, graphite, wood, and ice. In spite of this wide difference, however, it is found that the frictional properties of non-metals are fairly uniform, so that we may enumerate an average or typical frictional behavior, and then go on to consider how various individual substances diverge from the norm.

When unlubricated non-metals slide on themselves, they generally show kinetic friction coefficients (in the speed range 1 to 100 cm/sec) of 0.4 to 0.3, with static coefficients (time of contact 1 to 100 sec) in the range 0.6 to 0.4. The surface damage and wear are moderate, that is, smaller than for clean metals of comparable hardness. Naturally, the soft non-metals show more surface damage and wear under comparable conditions of load and distance of travel than do the harder non-metals. Non-metals generally have friction coefficients lowered by 0.1 or so when moist. Most non-metals give friction coefficients somewhat above 0.1 when well lubricated, whereas under comparable conditions metals give friction values of 0.04–0.10.

When non-metals are slid on other materials, either metal or non-metal, the frictional properties tend to be those of the softer material, and the nature of the harder material makes little difference. This is because the harder material, in most cases, becomes covered by particles of the softer one so that eventually our sliding system consists of the softer material sliding on itself.

Non-metals generally obey the laws of sliding friction, as outlined in Section 4.2. There are a number of divergences, however, from the average behavior outlined previously, almost all of which are explicable in terms of peculiarities in the mechanical properties of the substances in question, these mechanical properties being the result of exceptional structural factors. We shall enumerate some of the most prominent.

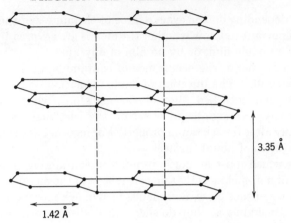

Fig. 4.27.   The atomic lattice of graphite.

Friction of highly elastic materials.   Many non-metals, including diamond (Bowden and Young, 1951), various polymers (Pascoe and Tabor, 1956) and MoS_2-resin combinations (Crump, 1956) give friction coefficients which diminish as the load is increased (Fig. 4.8). The explanation is based on the fact that these materials differ from the metals and many other non-metals in having high values of ϵ_y, the maximum elastic strain, and hence their deformation during sliding is elastic rather than plastic.

For elastically deformed junctions, we may make a limit analysis for the friction coefficient.   When the load is increased, there are generally two effects, namely that the size of the junctions increases and that their number increases.   If we have a system where the size increases but the number stays constant, the friction force for each junction, like A_r, will vary as the $\frac{2}{3}$ power of the load (eq. 3.3), whereas if the size of the junctions stays constant but their number varies, the friction force must vary as the first power of the load.   The actual values, depending on the geometry, will be somewhere between these two limits.   For a very detailed discussion, both theoretical and experimental, the reader is referred to Chapter 13 of Bowden and Tabor, 1964.

Friction of layer lattice materials.   In this category we may place graphite, molybdenum disulfide, and cadmium iodide.   These substances are rather different in their composition and type of chemical bonding, but they all have one thing in common, namely they all have a layer-lattice structure.   That is to say their crystal structure is such that sheets exist within their crystal lattices, within which the atoms are tightly packed and strongly bonded. These sheets are separated by relatively large distances, however, and held together by weak residual forces. For example, in graphite, a crystalline form of carbon, the distance of atoms within the sheets is 1.4×10^{-8} cm, but between sheets it is as much as 3.4×10^{-8} cm (Fig. 4.27). In consequence, although there are strong attractive forces within the graphite sheets, the forces holding the various sheets together are much weaker.

Graphite and other layer-lattice materials have low friction coefficients (about 0.1) when sliding takes place on a face parallel to the sheet direction, but much higher friction coefficients (about 0.3) when sliding takes place perpendicular to a face. When a multicrystalline block of graphite or another layer-lattice material is slid on a metal surface, it is found that platelets detach themselves from the graphite block and are deposited on the metal surface so that the sheets lie almost flat (see Fig. 4.28). This brings the favorable frictional properties of the layer lattice material into play (Savage, 1950).

With graphite, it is found that low friction and a low wear rate are developed only in the presence of moisture or of some volatile organic material. The function of this other substance is, apparently, to help in splitting off the layer-lattice platelets. In molybdenum disulfide, it appears that, under some conditions, no auxiliary material is required to allow the low friction condition to be maintained (Johnson and Vaughn, 1956).

The layer lattice materials make excellent solid film lubricants, either applied in powder form to solid surfaces, or preferably mixed with a strong resin binder and then "glued" to the surface.

Polytetrafluoroethylene (Teflon). This plastic is noted for its great chemical inertness because of the strong carbon-fluorine bonds in

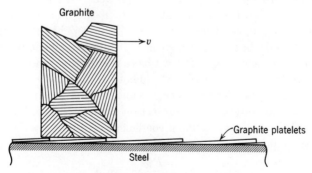

Fig. 4.28. When a composite block of graphite (random orientation) slides on a metal, an oriented film forms on the metal.

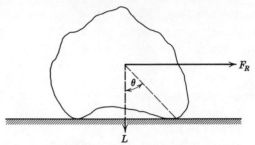

Fig. 4.29. Rolling friction force for an irregular object.

its structure. Accompanying this, we may note that it has a very low surface energy. Consequently, teflon has a "slippery" feel, and shows very little tendency to form strong bonds with other materials. Hence its friction coefficient is very low, and values down to 0.04 are commonly observed at high loads and low sliding velocities.

Boron nitride. We should not leave this section without pointing out that the frictional properties of some materials are *not* readily explained in terms of their structure. Thus boron nitride is very inert and shows very little tendency to form strong bonds with other materials (hardly any liquids wet boron nitride). Furthermore, it has a layer-lattice structure. In spite of these two features, it does not give especially low friction and does not make a good solid film lubricant (Rowe, 1960; Rabinowicz and Imai, 1964).

4.10   Rolling Friction

Rolling friction is the resistance to motion which takes place when an object is rolled over an abutting surface. We may at the outset distinguish between two separate cases, in the first, where the rolled body is of irregular outline, say a boulder or a pebble, and the second where the body has a smooth surface of high geometric perfection.

In the first case (Fig. 4.29) we have a situation where the force to initiate rolling movement F_R is equal to $L \tan \theta$, where L is the load and θ the angle between the vertical and the line joining the center of gravity of the body and the projection about which rolling is to take place. Hence we may define a coefficient of rolling friction f_R according to the equation

$$f_R = \frac{F_R}{L} = \tan \theta \qquad (4.12)$$

(It may be noted that if the sliding coefficient of friction between object and ground is less than tan θ, the application of a tangential force will produce sliding rather than rolling.)

As rolling continues, θ is changing, often taking on negative values. Hence the friction force to maintain rolling at constant velocity takes on positive as well as negative values. On the average, the force required to maintain rolling will be much less than the force required to start rolling, and hence the kinetic coefficient of rolling friction will be less than the static.

The term rolling friction, however, is usually restricted to bodies of near perfect shape and with very small surface roughness. For such bodies, the roughness component of the friction force is very low, and in consequence it is found that very low friction forces are observed, with rolling friction coefficients generally in the range 5.10^{-3} to 10^{-5}. This resistance to motion is not due to any one main cause, but rather to a combination of causes, each one of which tends to be more prominent in some circumstances, much less important in others. Taking them in turn, there are as follows.

Slip at the region of contact. If the contact of the two bodies (say a sphere on a flat surface, although other configurations are subject to the same considerations) were a point, we could consider pure rolling conditions to prevail. In practice, however, the region of contact is elastically (and in extreme cases) plastically deformed, so that contact is made over an area of some size, the points within it lying in different planes (Fig. 4.30). In consequence, it is not possible for pure rolling action to take place except at a very small number of points, but rather, at all other points, we have a combination of rolling combined with a small degree of sliding or slip. To achieve this slipping

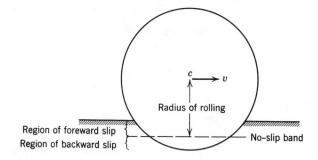

Fig. 4.30. A sphere is rolling on a flat surface. Note the regions of foreward and backward slippage.

requires that we overcome sliding resistance at the interface, and to accomplish this it is necessary that a rolling friction force act.

Although the slip velocities are generally small (usually 5% or less of the overall rolling velocity), this small amount of slip produces in many cases a major part of the total resistance to rolling. We may write an expression for the total rolling friction f_R in the form

$$f_R = \frac{v_s}{v_r} f_K \qquad (4.13)$$

where v_s is the slip velocity, v_r is the rolling velocity, and f_K the kinetic coefficient of sliding friction.

In some rolling contact systems (e.g., ball bearings, gear teeth), factors are present, besides the geometrical one of contact over an extended area, which tend to produce slip at the region of contact and thus raise the effective friction coefficient. In some cases the surfaces tend to spin about the region of contact, in others there is gross slippage. In such cases the rolling friction coefficient may be quite large, values greater than 10^{-3} being common.

Hysteresis losses. During rolling, different regions on the ball and the flat surface are first stressed, and then the stress is released as rolling continues and the point of contact moves on. Each time an element of volume in either body is stressed, elastic energy is taken up by it. Most of this energy is later released as the stress is removed from the element of the body, but a small part is lost (in the form of heat) owing to elastic hysteresis of the material of which the contacting bodies are made. This continued drain of energy must be made good by the rolling force, and thus yet another component is added to the rolling coefficient of friction.

This hysteresis component of the total rolling friction coefficient is small in some situations, that is, less than 10^{-4}, but, probably in the majority of situations it is a predominant contribution to the total rolling coefficient (Tabor, 1956; Drutowski, 1959).

Other friction losses during rolling. In this category we may place a number of miscellaneous processes, any or all of which may occur during rolling and use up energy. First, we may cite loss of energy caused by lack of perfection of the rolling geometry, for example lack of roundness of a bearing ball, or the presence of a dust particle in the rolling track. This will cause a "roughness component" of friction, just as we found earlier to exist with grossly irregular bodies, but on a smaller scale.

Second, we may cite energy losses caused by plastic deformation of asperities on the rolling surfaces, if these surfaces are not perfectly smooth. There will be analogous energy losses if contaminant particles are pressed into the rolling surfaces, or if they become ground up.

Third, there is the work which must be done to continually create free surface during rolling, as the interface of contact moves on.

Lastly, there are energy losses in many rolling contact systems which occur quite apart from the rolling action, the principal ones being sliding action at the interface between the retaining cage and the rolling balls and viscous losses in the liquid oil, or grease, which may be present.

All these losses add up to a component of the rolling friction force of the order of magnitude of 10^{-4}, that is, seldom predominant in magnitude, but often not negligible.

4.11 Laws of Rolling Friction

It is difficult to set down quantitative laws of rolling friction analogous to those of sliding friction, because each of the mechanisms ennumerated earlier has its own, quite different laws, and the overall coefficient of friction will depend on which components of the rolling friction force are the most important for the particular system under discussion. Some generalized remarks may be made, however.

1. The friction force varies as some power of the load, ranging from the 1.2 to the 2.4th. For lightly loaded systems where the deformation at the contact is purely elastic, the friction force generally varies as a low power of the load (say the 1.3). For heavily loaded systems where plastic deformation has occurred at the contacting area, the friction force varies as some higher power of the load, say the 2.0.

2. The friction force varies inversely with the radius of curvature of the rolling elements.

3. The friction force is lower for smoother surfaces than for rough surfaces. In fact, in almost every case, the friction of a rolling contact device drops during run-in, during which time the surface finish is being improved by the rolling action.

4. The static friction force is generally much greater than the kinetic, but the kinetic is little dependent on the rolling velocity, although it does generally drop off somewhat as the rolling velocity is increased.

As general summary we may say that the force of rolling friction is a very small fraction of the applied load and is caused by a number of diverse factors.

4.12   The Temperature of Sliding Surfaces

When surfaces slide together, almost all the energy dissipated in friction appears in the form of heat at the interface; indeed, historically speaking, it was a friction experiment which proved for the first time the equivalence of mechanical energy and heat.   This frictional heat raises the temperature of the interface above that of the environment.

In most sliding situations, as we have seen, contact is made, not over the whole of the apparent area of contact, but over a few isolated junctions.   Since these are small, and receive substantial amounts of thermal energy, their temperature may be much higher than that of neighboring surface regions.   The high temperature associated with the junctions is often referred to as the "flash temperature."   During sliding, junctions continue to be made and broken, and the "hot spots" on the surfaces shift their location.   The flash temperature reached at any of these hot spots, however, tends to be reasonably constant under constant sliding conditions.

In many cases, it is helpful to be able to calculate the flash temperatures which arise during sliding.   For example, if one of the materials in sliding contact has a mechanical strength which drops off drastically as the temperature is raised, it becomes important to calculate the maximum temperature reached during sliding (i.e., the temperature component which must be added to the bulk temperature of the material) to ascertain whether the material will be able to meet its structural requirements.   On other occasions a lubricant may be present which functions effectively only below a certain critical temperature,

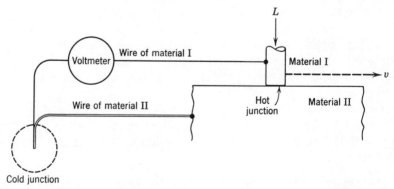

Fig. 4.31.   Schematic illustration of thermocouple method of measuring temperature at sliding interface.

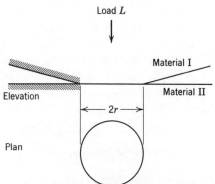

Fig. 4.32. Assumed junction model.

or which starts to decompose above certain temperatures. In all these cases, it is important to be able to calculate the maximum temperatures produced during sliding.

Although the maximum temperature is made up of two components, a bulk temperature rise and a flash temperature rise, we are usually more interested in the latter, since the former is usually less, and is generally quite readily measured. The latter represents a severe challenge, however. The best measurement technique consists in making the sliding interface we wish to study into one arm of a thermocouple, and this gives, after calibration of our materials, the average temperature at the junctions (Fig. 4.31). The method is not easy because many material combinations have but a low thermoelectric sensitivity, and in any case only dissimilar materials, both of which are electrical conductors, can be used for these measurements. Nevertheless, this technique has been used by a number of research workers, and the measured values for flash temperature rise generally agree with theoretical calculations within about 30%.

Generally, of course, we would much prefer to calculate rather than measure the flash temperatures of our surfaces. The necessary expression for calculating the flash temperature has been known for some time. In the greatly simplified case when the contact consists of one circular junction of diameter $2r$ sliding on a flat surface of another material (Fig. 4.32) at moderate speed, the interface attains an equilibrium mean temperature rise θ_m above the rest of the material given by

$$\theta_m = \frac{fLv}{4Jr(k_1 + k_2)} \tag{4.14}$$

where J is the mechanical equivalent of heat, and k_1 and k_2 are the thermal conductivities of the two contacting materials. This is a simplified expression which applies for moderate speeds. At really high speeds the temperature rise formula becomes more complex, and unsymmetrical, because far more heat flows into surface II, which continually sends new, cool, material into the zone where heat is generated, then into surface I, the same part of which always remains at the interface. If ρc is the volume specific heat, we have

$$\theta = \frac{fLv}{3.6rJ[1 \cdot 1k_2 + (\rho_1 \cdot c_1 \cdot rvk_1)^{\frac{1}{2}}]} \tag{4.15}$$

which at very high sliding velocities becomes

$$\theta = \frac{fLv^{\frac{1}{2}}}{3 \cdot 6J(\rho_1 \cdot c_1 \cdot r^3 k_1)^{\frac{1}{2}}} \tag{4.16}$$

Ordinarily, however, the simple eq. 4.14 may be used without too great error. (It should be pointed out that we have defined L as a force. Frequently, L is defined as a mass, and then the gravitational acceleration g appears in the numerator of eqs. 4.14 to 4.16.)

Three difficulties, one minor and two grave, unfortunately face anyone who wishes to carry through actual calculation of θ_m using eq. 4.14. First, he has to estimate the friction coefficient applicable to his sliding situation, which may introduce an uncertainty of 30% or thereabouts. Second, he has to estimate the size r of the junctions at which heat is actually being generated. An estimate here might easily be off by a factor of as much as 10. Third, he must allow in some way for the fact that heat is generated, not at one junction, but at many, which means that the load L at each junction must be calculated, and their mutual influence estimated.

In consequence of the difficulties involved in this situation, hardly anyone ever does try to calculate the temperature rise produced in sliding. Instead, if the author's consulting experience is typical, reliance is generally placed on one or another of two widely established but mutually exclusive maxims.

1. The flash temperature at a sliding surface is usually only a little greater than the average temperature of the contacting surfaces.

2. The flash temperature is usually the melting temperature of the lower melting of the two sliding materials.

To provide an order-of-magnitude realistic estimate of actual surface temperatures, the author has for a number of years used the simple (and crude) formula

$$\theta_m = \frac{v}{2} \ (\pm \text{ a factor of 3}) \tag{4.17}$$

where θ_m is the flash temperature (in °F), and v is the sliding speed in ft/min. This simple formula generally agrees to within about a factor of 2 or 3 with the temperature rise as measured experimentally, using the thermocouple methods shown in Fig. 4.31. This good agreement is especially surprising in that the eq. 4.14 contains parameters, such as the applied load and the junction diameter, that clearly vary a great deal from application to application.

4.13 Calculation of Flash Temperature Using Surface Energy Methods

For the first time, recent developments in the theory of the friction process have máde it possible to derive order-of-magnitude expressions for the sizes of junctions of surfaces in contact, and this has enabled us to attack the temperature rise formula again. According to these calculations (see Chapter 6) we may write an expression for the radius r of a junction in the form

$$r = 12{,}000 \ \frac{\gamma}{p} \tag{4.18}$$

where γ is the surface energy and p the hardness of the softer material.

Furthermore, for a typical sliding situation in which the total area of contact is determined by plastic deformation of the softer material, we have the load L carried by each junction and the radius of each junction related by the equation

$$L = \pi r^2 p \tag{4.19}$$

If we substitute for L, and then for the product rp, in eq. 4.14, we obtain as our final expression

$$\theta_m = \frac{\pi f \times 3000 \gamma v}{J(k_1 + k_2)} = \frac{9400 f \gamma v}{J(k_1 + k_2)} \tag{4.20}$$

This expression contains, apart from the sliding velocity, no parameter that is not a material constant or a conversion factor. If now we make the final assumption, justified for most sliding situations except a few very heavily loaded ones, that each of the individual junctions is so far away that it does not substantially influence the flash tempera-

Table 4.1.   Computed Temperature Rise Per Unit Sliding Velocity

Material Combination	f	γ	k_1	k_2	θ/v (°C/cm/sec)
Steel on steel	0.5	1500	0.11	0.11	0.75
Lead on steel	0.5	450	0.08	0.11	0.26
Bakelite on bakelite	0.3	100	0.0015	0.0015	2.2
Brass on brass	0.4	900	0.26	0.26	0.15
Glass on steel	0.3	500	0.0007	0.11	0.3
Steel on nylon	0.3	120	0.11	0.0006	0.07
Brass on nylon	0.3	120	0.26	0.0006	0.03
Steel on bronze	0.25	900	0.11	0.18	0.17

ture of its neighbors, then eq. 4.20 becomes the final value for the flash temperature.

In applying eq. 4.20 we may be faced by a problem of units. The friction coefficient, of course, is a pure number, but γ, the surface tension of the softer sliding member, is generally given in units of dynes/cm, and then if k is given in c.g.s. units of cal/°C.cm.sec., and v in cm/sec, θ will be in °C if J is in ergs/cal. Some typical values for temperature rise, in °C/cm/sec sliding speed are worked out in the Table 4.1. In all cases, I have assumed unlubricated surfaces, as the effect of a lubricant is a little difficult to allow for.

It will be seen that θ/v values are far more uniform than are the individual values of γ and k, because non-metals, which have relatively low values of k, also have low values of γ. Thus the θ/v ratio tends toward constancy, and inspection of the table shows that the various θ/v values generally range within a factor of about 3 around a value of 0.5 °C/cm/sec. This corresponds to a value of about 0.45 °F/ft/min. This, then, provides some sort of theoretical backing for the empirical relationship of eq. 4.17. (Note that rather lower values of θ/v are obtained when a metal is slid on a soft non-metal).

Although the concept of the flash temperature rise as defined by eq. 4.20 is still very new, and must be experimentally tested in a wide variety of practical situations, it does serve to put empirical relationships such as eq. 4.17 on a sounder theoretical basis. The fact that there is some kind of direct relationship between sliding speed and the temperature rise is one that many engineers can use to advantage.

4.14   The Relation between Temperature and Friction

In this section we shall examine the changes in friction produced as a result of a change in temperature. There are two different types of temperature change to be considered. The first is the case where we have two sliding bodies and change their bulk temperature by external heating or cooling; the second is the situation considered in the previous section where the temperature rise is caused by high-speed sliding, so that we have a hot surface layer superposed on a colder substrate.

We may dismiss the second case with the comment that during high-speed sliding the friction coefficient is generally low because s in eq. 4.6 is low while p is high. If the sliding speed is so high that some surface melting occurs (generally referred to as melt lubrication, Sternlicht and Apkarian, 1960), friction coefficients under 0.1 are frequently observed (Bowden and Freitag, 1958).

For externally applied temperature changes, we note that the friction coefficient is basically insensitive to those temperature variations which merely affect the mechanical strengths of the sliding bodies, because both the shear strength and the hardness terms of eq. 4.6 are affected to the same degree. This indeed is borne out by the experiments of Simon, McMahon, and Bowen (1951), who found no systematic trend in the friction between $-270°C$ and $+300°C$. A similar result in shown in Fig. 4.33 which shows a plot of the mean of 50 high temperature friction tests of the author's, covering a wide range of

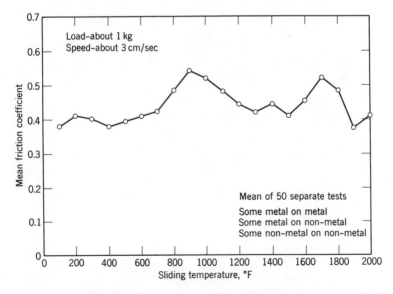

Fig. 4.33. Mean friction coefficient as a function of sliding temperature as derived from 50 widely varying material combinations. Essentially, friction is not a temperature-dependent quantity.

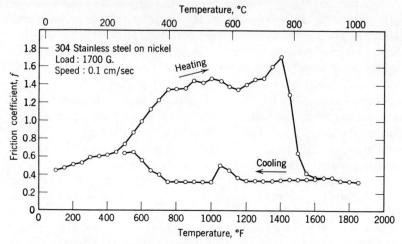

Fig. 4.34. Friction as a function of temperature for stainless steel on nickel. The nickel oxide layer formed at 1500°F persists on cooling.

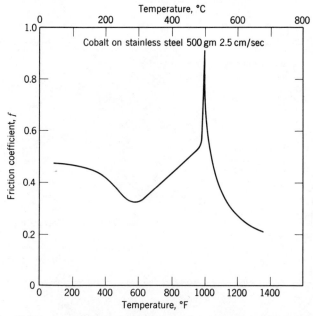

Fig. 4.35. Friction as a function of temperature for cobalt on stainless steel. The peak in friction at 1000°F may be associated with the change from Co_3O_4 to CoO oxide species (Foley, Peterson, and Zapf, 1963).

materials.   Although the individual tests show considerable change in friction as the temperature is raised, the mean of all the tests shows essentially no variation.

Some of the causes of variations in friction as the temperature is increased, starting from room temperature, are as follows:

1. With metal combinations which show severe frictional interaction, a drop in friction from about 1.0 to about 0.5 is observed, usually over a narrow temperature range.   This drop is caused by the formation of a thick oxide layer and reduced metallic interaction (Fig. 4.34).   If sliding is continued while the temperature is reduced, a characteristic 'hysteresis loop' develops (Peterson, Florek, and Lee, 1960).

2. With many metals there are changes in the friction, either upward or downward, as one predominant oxide species is replaced by another which has greater or lesser lubricating ability (Fig. 4.35).

3. It is universally observed that a rise in friction takes place as the melting temperature of one of the bodies is approached (Fig. 4.36). This rise occurs because the ratio γ/v for the lower-melting body, and

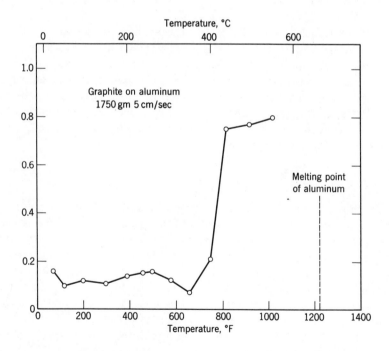

Fig. 4.36.   Friction-temperature plot for graphite on aluminum.   Note the rise in friction as the melting temperature of aluminum is approached.

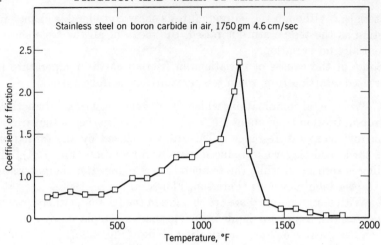

Fig. 4.37.   The peak in the friction when boron carbide is heated is due to the formation of "sticky" boric oxide.

consequently the ratio W_{ab}/p for the system, increases rapidly as temperatures up to the melting point are reached (since γ is little affected by temperature whereas p goes to zero at the melting point).

4. For sliding systems where a surface coating is formed which passes through a tacky stage, there is a peak in the friction corresponding to this tacky stage.   Thus boron carbide, which forms a boric oxide film when heated in air, gives a friction peak while the boric oxide is a high viscosity glass (Fig. 4.37).

4.15   Stick-Slip

It is a matter of common experience that the sliding of one body over another under a steady pulling force proceeds sometimes at constant or nearly constant velocity, on other occasions at velocities that fluctuate widely.   In most practical sliding systems these fluctuations of the sliding velocity are considered a serious nuisance, and measures are normally taken to eliminate, or at any rate to reduce, the amplitude of the fluctuations.   A study of the factors which determine the nature of the motion of sliding systems is of interest not only as a practical matter, but also in throwing light into the intrinsic characteristic of the sliding process.

All stick-slip processes are caused by the fact that the friction force does not remain constant as a function of some other variable.   This

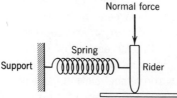

Fig. 4.38. Representation of a typical friction apparatus.

other variable may be distance, time, or velocity, and each produces a form of oscillation.

Irregular stick-slip—displacement controlled. We may take Fig. 4.38 to represent a typical sliding situation involving one body (called the rider) fixed to a stationary support by means of a spring, the other being a surface (the flat) in motion under a constant velocity v. We will initially suppose that this velocity is sufficiently low so that the rider has no difficulty in keeping up with the movement of the flat, and that the damping is negligible.

Suppose that the intrinsic plot of friction force as a function of displacement for this rider on the flat is as shown in Fig. 4.39. Since this is a force-displacement plot, we may on the same diagram indicate the force-displacement function of the spring, which for any position of the rider will be a straight line of slope -k through that point. If we start the run at B the rider will move over the flat at constant velocity (fluctuating slightly since the position of the rider changes somewhat as the friction force changes) until the point C is reached. Here the friction force drops abruptly. The rider tries to adjust its position

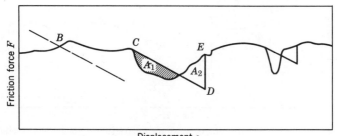

Fig. 4.39. Hypothetical force-displacement plot.

accordingly, but the best that the spring will allow it to do is to follow the straight line shown. Hence the shaded area in the diagram, denoting a discrepancy between the two curves, is produced. This area has the dimensions of energy, and represents excess energy in the system which becomes kinetic energy of the rider. The rider thus is set into motion and slips, and will continue to move until D is reached. At this point the area above the friction force curve is equal to the area below it (subject to a small allowance for air damping during slip), and thus all the kinetic energy has been used up. The spring force is now well below the friction force, so that the rider will stick to the flat and be dragged along by it to E, where the friction force becomes large enough to initiate relative motion again.

If we plot the friction force as a function of time, the plot will look as shown in Fig. 4.40. Traces of this kind will be denoted as "irregular stick-slip," and occur very frequently with clean, like metals (Fig. 4.23).

If we make our spring so stiff that its slope in Fig. 4-39 is greater than the maximum slope of the f–s plot, irregular stick-slip is automatically prevented. To illustrate this point, Fig. 4.41 has been produced showing two traces, one obtained with a loose, the other with a tight spring.

The two main conditions under which irregular stick-slip is observed are the sliding of clean metals, (severe frictional behavior), and the sliding of metals covered by a solid film lubricant which has been partially worn away. In the sliding of clean metals the large fluctuations in friction arise because the junctions in the contact area coalesce to form one or at most a few superjunctions, and this process is a prerequisite for the occurrence of severe fluctuations of the friction force. In the second case the fluctuations arise because the rider traverses

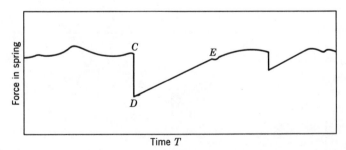

Fig. 4.40. Friction record corresponding to friction-displacement relationship of Fig. 4.34.

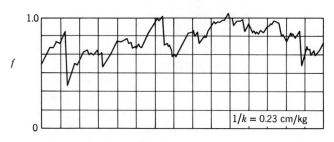

Cu on Cu 1000 gm 0.15 cm/sec

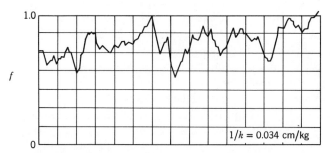

Fig. 4.41. Actual friction traces produced under otherwise identical conditions using loose and tight springs.

alternatively regions covered by the film and regions from which the film is absent.

Regular stick-slip—time controlled. This, the classical form of stick slip, can arise whenever the static coefficient of friction is markedly greater than the kinetic coefficient. If we take a sliding situation in which the plate velocity is low compared to the maximum rider velocity during the slip, and in which the external damping is negligible, we may develop a simple model of stick-slip behaviour. We assume that the static coefficient of friction is a function of time of contact (Ishlinski and Kraghelsky, 1944), as shown in Fig. 4.42, but that the kinetic coefficient remains a constant. As justification for the shape of the curve we note that Sampson, Morgan, Reed, and Muskat (1943) have shown that the static coefficient for small times of stationary contact is equal to the kinetic, whereas the data of Dokos (1946) plotted in Fig. 4.43 show that the plot of f_s against log t approximates to a straight line, indicating that for small values of t the slope of the curve in Fig. 4.42 must be very steep, for large values very small.

If we place our surfaces together and set the flat in motion at a velocity v, the spring force increases with time at a rate kvt, and this may be plotted in Fig. 4.42 as a straight line through the origin with slope kv/L. At point A, slip occurs, and since the kinetic coefficient is assumed constant, we have a situation where slip continues to point B, as far below the f_k line as A was above it. At B the rider comes to rest, which we plot as point C, and the next stick-cycle takes us to D, E, and F. Finally, a steady state is reached. If we increase v or k, our line becomes steeper and the stick-slip will have a smaller amplitude.

Harmonic oscillations—velocity controlled. These oscillations are observed mainly at high sliding velocities. Their characteristic feature is that the rider vibrates in a manner which closely approximates to a simple harmonic oscillation, but the relative velocity between the rider and the flat never reaches zero. It is a prerequisite for this form of oscillation that, at the sliding velocity v, the f–v curves have a negative slope. During one-half of the cycle, energy is transferred from the flat to the rider, during the other half, energy is transferred from the rider to the flat, and owing to the negative characteristic there is a positive difference between the two which is dissipated by damping.

The negative f–v slopes observed at high speeds are connected with thermal softening, which produces a low-shear surface film on a harder substrate. In calculating the details of the oscillation, we are

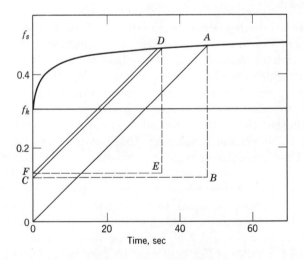

Fig. 4.42.   Static coefficient plotted against time of stick.

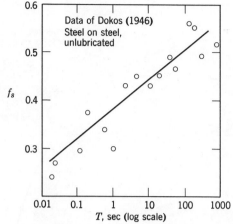

Fig. 4.43.   Plot of static coefficient against time of stick.

faced with a complicated problem since the friction coefficient is determined by the instantaneous surface temperature, but this is based on the whole previous sliding history.

4.16   Prevention of Stick-Slip

Reducing stick-slip amplitude.   A number of methods for preventing stick-slip are in use.   First, there are the methods which decrease the amplitude of the slip, or the sliding velocity during the slip, either by increased damping, by increased inertia, or by increased stiffness of the spring.   The surprising thing is not that these methods reduce the stick-slip amplitude—we expect them to do that—but that in many cases they eliminate stick-slip completely.

We have studied this process using an apparatus with which we can vary the stiffness of the spring shown in Fig. 4.38.   Thus we can carry out sliding experiments with spring stiffness as our main variable.

Figure 4.44 shows the results of tests using steel on steel, unlubricated.   The slip amplitude is plotted as a function of velocity for each of four spring stiffnesses.   Note that the slip amplitude does not diminish slowly, but rather that it drops to zero abruptly.   Calculations suggest that the slip ceases whenever conditions are such that the displacement between the surfaces during slip would be less than about 10^{-3} cm, and this is in line with previous work suggesting that, when starting at rest, sliding through this distance is necessary to

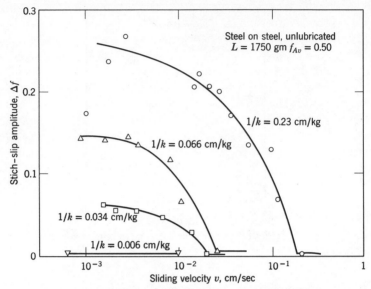

Fig. 4.44. Stick-slip amplitude for various spring stiffnesses.

allow the higher static coefficient of friction to drop to the lower value characteristic of sliding surfaces (Rabinowicz, 1951). In fact, the distance of 10^{-3} cm represents the size of the junctions of the steel-on-steel system.

Ensuring a positive f–v curve. The second main method of preventing stick-slip is to try to arrange to have a positive friction-velocity characteristic at the sliding velocity employed. This does not ensure the prevention of stick-slip in principle, if the f_s–t and the f_k–v curves are assumed to be independent. If, as seems highly probable, they are related, it is difficult to imagine a situation where the f_k–v curve is positive and the f_s–t curve is so also. In fact the whole concept of static coefficient is meaningless for a positive f_k–v curve. Thus it becomes of great interest to examine f_k–v curves systematically.

For unlubricated titanium on titanium, the friction-velocity characteristic is negative over the whole speed range (Fig. 4.12), and similar results are obtained with other hard metals like copper and steel. On the other hand, soft metals like lead and indium have positive characteristics at low speeds, changing to negative slopes as the speed is raised (Fig. 4.13). Lead has its maximum at around 10^{-6} cm/sec, whereas the still softer indium has its maximum at 10^{-4} cm/sec. Other materials, including various rubbers, soap, plastics, etc., all show the same behavior, namely a positive characteristic at low speeds and a negative characteristic at high speeds, and this seems to be a general property of all materials. Within any class it is found that the hard materials have their maxima at very low speeds, and that, as softer and softer materials are used, the maxima are shifted to higher and higher speeds. To give but one illustration, nylon, a hard plastic, has its maximum at a speed of the order of 10^{-3} cm/sec, Teflon, a soft plastic, has its maximum near 10^1 cm/sec. This result may be explained by assuming that the positive slope is caused by a creep, and the negative slope by an adhesion, mechanism. As we raise the stress we raise the creep velocity in the one case, and as we shorten the time of contact for any junction we decrease the strength of adhesion in the other. The softer materials may be expected to have higher creep velocities than the others, confirming our experimental results.

To give a hard material the favorable f–v slope of a soft one, we may place a thin film of soft material on the harder one, since, when a soft film is placed on a hard substrate, the slope of the f–v curve is determined primarily by the surface film. The disadvantage of this method of lubrication is that the applied surface film is not permanent, and as it is gradually removed during sliding stick-slip again becomes possible. Figure 4.45 illustrates thepo int, and shows f–v curves for unlubricated

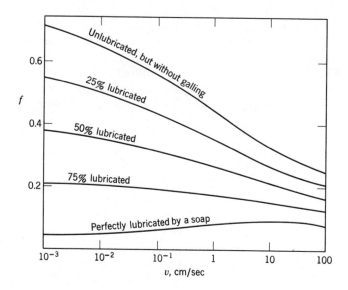

Fig. 4.45. Experimental friction-velocity curves for steel on steel, unlubricated and perfectly lubricated by a soap, also derived curves for intermediate stages of lubrication.

steel on steel, and for steel on steel perfectly lubricated by copper palmitate. If the copper palmitate has been worn off 50% of the sliding track, the friction-velocity curve will be that lying half-way between these two extremes, and similarly for other per cent coverages. By the time the film has been removed, to the extent the lubricant coverage is down to 90%, the friction coefficient is about 0.09 to 0.11 over the whole range of velocities shown in Fig. 4.45, and the friction characteristic is neither positive or negative. For all lower values of lubricant coverage stick-slip is possible in principle; the average stick-slip apparatus normally allows stick-slip when lubricant coverage is below about 80 to 85%, that is, at friction coefficients of about 0.15. This is the basis underlying the use of stick-slip occurrence to signify lubricant breakdown; that is, when a sliding system squeaks or squeals, it needs to be relubricated.

4.17   The Measurement of Friction

The simplest parameter to measure is the force required to initiate sliding, which can then be readily converted to the static friction coefficient. In the tilting plane arrangement the normal force varies and the friction angle θ is measured directly (Fig. 4.46, 4.47), but it is also quite simple to keep the load constant and to increase the pulling force until sliding commences (Fig. 4.48, 4.49). Measurements of this type are frequently carried out, their main limitation being that it is difficult to prevent shock loading and to keep the time of sticking under control.

For measuring the friction during sliding it is customary to use a dynamometer method, in which the force required to keep one body stationary, when pressed against a moving surface, is monitored (Fig.

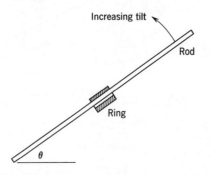

Fig. 4.46.   A form of the tilting plane apparatus (useful for tests in vacuo).

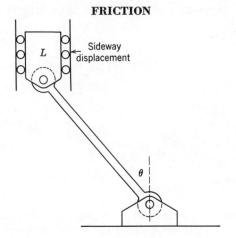

Fig. 4.47. An adaptation of the tilting plane (for measuring slipperyness of floors).

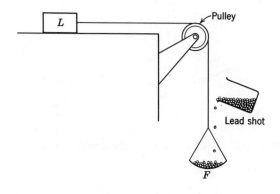

Fig. 4.48. Weight-and-pulley method of measuring static friction.

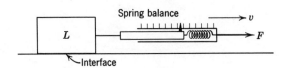

Fig. 4.49. Simple spring balance method of measuring static and kinetic friction. (A very simple versatile method. I have used it for measuring the slipperyness of floors).

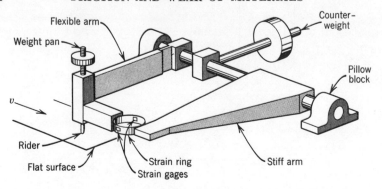

Fig. 4.50. Friction measurement with a dynamometer. The friction force compresses the strain ring. (This is probably the best all-purpose way of measuring friction in the laboratory).

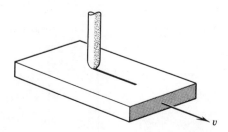

Fig. 4.51. Translating geometry (usually single-pass).

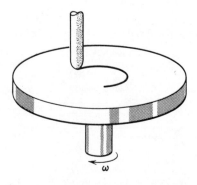

Fig. 4.52. Rotating geometry (usually multiple-pass).

4.50). Normally, the friction force is recorded continuously. An arrangement of this type, or one similar to this, is used for geometries of a pin on a translating flat (Fig. 4.51), pin on a rotating flat (Fig. 4.52), or a cylinder on another cylinder (Fig. 4.53).

It will be noticed that in all these methods the contact has been localized so that sliding takes place over a narrow track. In fact, in many cases the track is narrowed further by tapering or rounding off the end of the pin so that initially the apparent and real areas of contact are equal. This makes it easy to locate areas on the surface, for microscopic examination for example, and the friction coefficients ob-

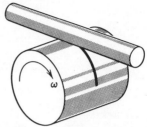

Fig. 4.53. One cylinder contacting another cylinder.

tained in this way will be valid for less concentrated loading systems, as long as the friction force is independent of the apparent area of contact.

When we are interested in tests which approach more closely to those prevailing in actual bearing applications, we often choose the geometry of one cylinder whose end contacts the end of another cylinder. To localize the contact somewhat so that friction torque measurements can be converted into friction coefficients, one or both cylinders have a recessed center (Fig. 4.54). A hybrid between this arrangement and the single pin-on-flat described above is seen in the 3 pin on a flat geometry (Fig. 4.55). Somewhat analogous to this

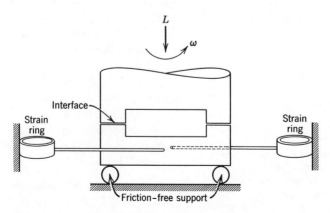

Fig. 4.54. Concentric cylinder method of measuring friction.

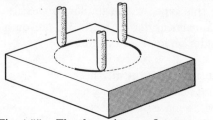

Fig. 4.55.   The three-pin-on-a-flat geometry.

last arrangement is the 4-ball apparatus, in which one bearing ball rotates on three fixed ones (Fig. 4.56).

In most experiments the friction coefficient is studied as a function of one or another of the following variables.

Variation of friction with time of sliding.   This generally constitutes the study of the wear of some surface coating, or the deterioration of some material present in the sliding system.   Alternatively, we might try to study the properties of junctions by measuring fluctuations in the friction force (Section 3.5).

Variation of the friction coefficient with load.   Any departure from the first quantitative law of friction is of interest, and, if the coefficient increases as the load increases, severe sliding behavior or even seizing may be imminent.

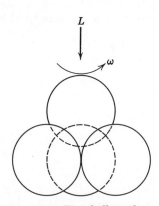

Fig. 4.56.   The ball-on-three-ball geometry. The lower three balls are kept fixed. In another version, used for studying rolling friction, the three lower balls are allowed to rotate inside a cylindrical "cup."

Variation of friction with sliding speed.   When moderate sliding speeds are used, it is possible to study the tendency toward stick-slip by measuring the slope of the friction-velocity curve. Stick-slip itself can be studied by using a dynamometer whose spring constant may be varied.

At high speeds, the high interface temperature causes softening or melting, and then we come into the region of melt lubrication.

Variation of friction with temperature.   Experiments on the effect of temperature require some arrangement for heating the surfaces.   At very high temperatures (above about 600°F) it is necessary to build a friction apparatus into a furnace. Tests in which the temperature is varied indicate the desorption point of lubricants, the formation of oxides and perhaps other films, and help to determine the usefulness of materials under high temperature sliding conditions.

Variation of friction with degree of vacuum. These tests also require special apparatus, and are most useful in extending theories of friction, and in selecting materials for use in sliding applications related to outer space.

References

Allan, A. J. G. (1958), Plastics as Solid Lubricants and Bearings, *Lubrication Engineering*, **14**, 211–215.

Archard, J. F. and W. Hirst (1956), The Wear of Metals under Unlubricated Conditions, *Proc. Roy. Soc.*, A **236**, 397–410.

Avient, B. W. E., J. Goddard, and H. Wilman (1960), An Experimental Study of Friction and Wear during Abrasion of Metals, *Proc. Roy. Soc.*, A **258**, 159–180.

Bowden, F. P., and E. H. Freitag (1958), The Friction of Solids at Very High Speeds, *Proc. Roy. Soc.*, A **248**, 350–367.

Bowden, F. P., and T. P. Hughes (1939), Friction of Clean Metals and Influence of Adsorbed Gases, *Proc. Roy. Soc.*, A **172**, 263–279.

Bowden, F. P., and D. Tabor (1954), *The Friction and Lubrication of Solids*, Clarendon Press, Oxford, Part I.

Bowden, F. P., and D. Tabor (1964), *The Friction and Lubrication of Solids*, Clarendon Press, Oxford, Part II.

Bowden, F. P., and J. E. Young (1951), Friction of Clean Metals and the Influence of Adsorbed Films, *Proc. Roy. Soc.*, A **208**, 311–325.

Burwell, J. T., and E. Rabinowicz (1953), The Nature of the Coefficient of Friction, *J. Appl. Phys.* **24**, 136–139.

Coffin, L. (1956), A Study of the Sliding of Metals, with Particular Reference to Atmosphere, *Lubrication Engineering.*, **12**, 50–59.

Courtney-Pratt, J. S., and E. Eisner (1957), The Effect of a Tangential Force on the Contact of Metallic Bodies, *Proc. Roy. Soc.* A **238**, 529–550.

Crump, R. E. (1956), Solid Film Lubricants—Factors Influencing their Mechanism of Friction and Wear, *Am. Soc. Lubrication Eng.*, Paper 56 LC-8.

Daniels, R. O., and A. C. West (1955), The Influence of Moisture on the Friction and Surface Damage of Clean Metals, *Lubrication Engineering*, **11**, 261–266.

Dokos, S. J. (1946), Sliding Friction under Extreme Pressures, *J. Appl. Mechanics*, **13**, A148–A156.

Drutowski, R. C. (1959), Energy Losses of Balls Rolling on Plates, pp. 16–35 of *Friction and Wear*, ed. by R. Davies, Elsevier, Amsterdam.

Ernst, H., and M. E. Merchant (1940), Surface Friction between Metals—a Basic Factor in the Metal Cutting Process, *Proc. Special Summer Conf. Friction and Surface Finish*, M.I.T., 76–101.

Foley, R. T., M. B. Peterson, and C. Zapf (1963), Frictional Characteristics of Cobalt, Nickel and Iron as Influenced by Their Surface Oxide Films, *Trans. Am. Soc. Lubrication Eng.*, **6**, 29–39.

Goodzeit, C. L., R. P. Hunnicutt, and A. E. Roach (1956), Frictional Characteristics and Surface Damage of Thirty-Nine Different Elemental Metals in
Sliding Contact with Iron, *Trans. Am. Soc. Mech. Eng.* **78,** 1669–1676.

Gwathmey, A. T. (1951), The Study of the Fundamentals of Lubrication with the
Aid of Large Metal Crystals, *Ann. New York Acad. Sci.,* **53,** 987–994.

Halaunbrenner, M. (1960), Directional Effects in Friction, *Wear,* **3,** 421–425.

Hanson, M. (1958), *Constitution of Binary Alloys,* 2nd Ed., McGraw-Hill, New
York.

Ishlinski, A. Y., and I. V. Kraghelsky (1944), On Stick-Slip in Friction (in Russian),
Zhur. Tekhn. Fiz., **14,** 276–282.

Johnson, V. R. and G. W. Vaughn (1956), Investigation of the Mechanism of
MoS_2 Lubrication in Vacuum, *J. Appl. Phys.,* **27,** 1173–1179.

Machlin, E. S., and W. R. Yankee (1954), Friction of Clean Metals and Oxides
with Special Reference to Titanium, *J. Appl. Phys.,* **25,** 576–581.

Pascoe, M. W., and D. Tabor (1956), The Friction and Deformation of Polymers,
Proc. Roy. Soc., **A 235,** 210–224.

Peterson, M. G., J. J. Florek, and R. E. Lee (1960), Sliding Characteristics of
Metals at High Temperatures, *Trans. Am. Soc. Lubrication Eng.,* **3,** 101–115.

Rabinowicz, E. (1951), The Nature of the Static and Kinetic Coefficients of Friction, *J. Appl. Phys.,* **22,** 1373–1379.

Rabinowicz, E. (1954), Frictional Properties of Titanium and Its Alloys, *Metal
Progress,* **65,** 107–110.

Rabinowicz, E. (1956), The Equilibrium Distribution of Transfer Fragments,
Lubrication Engineering, **12,** 401–404.

Rabinowicz, E (1957), Direction of the Friction Force, *Nature,* **179,** 1073.

Rabinowicz, E., and M. Imai (1964), Frictional Properties of Pyrolytic Boron
Nitride and Graphite, *Wear,* **7,** 296–298.

Rankin, J. S. (1926), The Elastic Range of Friction, *Phil. Mag.,* 7th Series, 806–816.

Roach, A. E., C. L. Goodzeit, and R. P. Hunnicutt (1956), Scoring Characteristics
of Thirty-Eight Different Elemental Metals in High-Speed Sliding Contact
with Steel, *Trans. Am. Soc. Mech. Eng.,* **78,** 1659–1667.

Rowe, G. W. (1960), Some Observations on the Frictional Behavior of Boron
Nitride and Graphite, *Wear,* **3,** 274–285.

Sampson, J. B., F. Morgan, D. W. Reed, and M. Muskat (1943), Friction Behavior
During the Slip Portion of the Stick-Slip Process, *J. Appl. Phys.,* **14,** 689–700.

Savage, R. H. (1950), The Vapor Lubrication of Graphite in Relation to Carbon
Brush Wear, pp. 95–108 of *Mechanical Wear,* ed. by J. T. Burwell, American
Society for Metals.

Schnurmann, R. and E. Wardlow-Davies (1942), The Electrostatic Component of
the Force of Sliding Friction, *Proc. Phys. Soc. (London).* **54,** 14–27.

Simon, I., H. O. McMahon, and R. J. Bowen (1951), Dry Metallic Friction as a
Function of Temperature between $4.2°K$ and $600°K$, *J. Appl. Phys.* **22,**
177–184.

Sternlicht, B., and H. Apkarian (1960), Investigation of 'Melt Lubrication', *Trans.
Am. Soc. Lubrication Eng.,* **2,** 248–256.

Stevens, J. S. (1899), Molecular Contact, *Phys. Rev.,* **8,** 49–56.

Tabor, D. (1956), The Mechanism of "Free" Rolling Friction, *Lubrication Engineering,* **12,** 379–386.

Whitehead, J. R. (1950), Surface Deformation and Friction of Metals at Light
Loads, *Proc. Roy. Soc.,* **A 201,** 109–124.

5

Types of Wear

5.1 Introduction; Economic Role of Wear

Although wear is an important topic, it has never received the attention it deserves. Accordingly, it may be worthwhile to commence our discussion by reviewing the economic role of wear.

There are three main ways in which inanimate objects lose their usefulness: obsolescence, breakage, and wear. Naturally, different classes of objects feel the impact of these three factors to different degrees. Thus, to take a first example, there is a lady's hat. This almost invariably becomes obsolete before any other reason for discardment becomes obvious. Second, we might consider a clinical thermometer, which continues in service until, one day, it breaks. Third, there is the phonograph needle, which is generally used until it wears out.

These examples are simple articles in which one cause for abandonment operates almost to the exclusion of the others. In many cases, however, especially with complex mechanisms, two or even all three effects are important. Thus an automobile may continue in service until it is traded in because it no longer looks stylish (obsolescence), or because it has been involved in a serious accident (breakage), or because it no longer performs well. It is this last possibility that constitutes loss of usefulness as a result of wear.

Wear may be defined as the removal of material from solid surfaces as a result of mechanical action. It is a characteristic feature of the wear process that the amount of material removed is quite small. Thus, although obsolescence and breakage in an automobile are readily visible, wear may be quite undetectable by casual inspection.   In fact, by the time a modern 4000-lb automobile is completely worn out, only a few ounces will have been worn off those surfaces which are in sliding contact.   However, although wear in sliding systems is usually a very slow process, it is very steady and continuous.   The terminology applicable to clothing, which equates use with wear, is very apt.

This discussion has established the importance of wear as one of the three mechanisms leading to the abandonment of material objects. For complicated objects, in fact, it is almost always the most important mechanism.   Nevertheless, there has been an almost total lack of interest in the wear phenomenon and lack of appreciation of its importance.   Thus, of the general encyclopedias published in the United States, none has an entry under wear.   Even engineering handbooks and similar works of reference preserve an almost total silence on the subject of wear.

This strange situation is the result of the historically very late study of the process of wear and the very recent elucidation (which, as we shall see in later chapters, is not yet completed) of the laws of wear. For this situation we may cite three reasons.   The first is that in former times wear was a much less important factor in determining the useful lives of machines and other mechanisms than it is today. Thus, if we compare the cylinder of a steam engine of the 1760's with the cylinder of an automobile engine of today, we note that although the horse-power of the two engines is comparable, the design is quite different.   Thus, the cylinder of 1760 worked at quite moderate steam pressures, and in any case had machining errors of at least $\frac{3}{8}$ in., so that even a considerable amount of wear (say $\frac{1}{4}$ in.) would not affect its performance greatly.   The automobile engine's cylinders, on the other hand, must, together with the piston, contain gas at very high pressure, and hence the cylinders are machined accurate to within one-thousandth of an inch and are worn out by the time that wear of the cylinder walls has reached about fifteen-thousandths of an inch. Hence, smaller amounts of wear in modern engines can be tolerated.

Second, there is the fact that wear rates are often quite low, so that until recently there was no ready way of studying any wear process continuously.   All that could be done was to measure or weigh the parts before the experiments, repeat this procedure after the experiment was over, and note the difference.   Only the advent of radio-isotopes of the common engineering metals, which may be dated to the building of nuclear piles in the 1940's, has placed a new technique into the hands of research workers, this technique having for the first time a resolution adequate for the study of wear while it was occurring (Rabinowicz and Tabor, 1951).

Third, there was the attitude on the part of many engineers and scientists that wear is a phenomenon, so complicated and erratic, that systematic investigation was bound to be a waste of time, and, hence, that the best thing to do in designing a new device was to rely on previous experience, to carry out a few life tests on the device itself and then to trust to luck. By and large, this attitude is still held by the majority of design engineers today. It works well when a new design represents but a minor change of an older successful design, but it is extremely dangerous when completely new situations are encountered; for example, the sliding motion of mechanisms to operate in outer space.

5.2 Uses of Wear

The wear process is generally thought of as a harmful one, and, indeed, in the majority of practical situations this is the case. There are, however, a considerable number of practical uses of the wear phenomenon.

The production of surfaces. Many methods of producing a surface on a manufactured object make use of the wear phenomenon. First, there is the family of abrasive processes, of which we may mention the use of files, of abrasive paper, and of loose abrasive grains on lapping and polishing wheels. By using a graduated series of files, or of abrasive paper, it is possible to cut material rapidly at first, using a coarse cutting agent, and then progressively to use finer grades, so that eventually a very smooth surface is produced.

A useful method of altering the finish of a surface is sand blasting. In this process abrasive grains are thrown at a surface, and leave it clean and rough, ready to receive a surface paint or coating.

Writing. A number of ways of recording information depend for their effectiveness on the wear process. Thus, the use of a pencil, of a crayon, or of a piece of chalk, are all dependent on the occurrence of adhesive wear. Anyone who has ever tried to write with chalk on a greasy blackboard (the grease acting as a wear preventative), knows how important it is that a high enough rate of wear is maintained.

A rubber eraser, with a certain degree of poetic justice, removes writing debris, also by an adhesive wear mechanism. First the carbon particle from the pencil is transferred by an adhesive wear mechanism to the surface of the eraser, and then the surface of the eraser is transferred by an adhesive wear mechanism to the paper, leaving a clean surface behind.

The preservation of sharp edges. In cutting operations it is essential that the cutting tool have a sharp edge. If, during cutting, the edge becomes blunted, cutting no longer occurs; the process must be stopped, and the edge must be re-formed. In some cases, however, wear acts so as to continually re-form the edge, so that effective cutting action can continue.

In one arrangement, used in electric shavers and meat grinders, adhesive wear along the bottom face acts so as to keep the cutting edge sharp (Fig. 5.1).

A second method, most elegant, is seen in animals of the rodent family, for example, the rabbit. The incisor teeth of these animals are covered with hard enamel along the outer curved surface, but there is only soft dentine on the inside. Hence, abrasive and adhesive wear, which occurs more rapidly on the softer side, always acts to maintain the sharpness of the tooth, (Fig. 5.2). A few man-made cutting tools have been made using this elegant principle of self-sharpening, including tungsten carbide-coated knives and plows with one hardened flank.

Use of wear in diagnosis. In many systems it is possible to make use of the wear phenomenon to study the progress of some event which occurred in a system while that system was in operation. The advantage of using the wear process in this way is that observations may be carried out while the system is not in operation, or even, in the case of failed systems, when it is no longer capable of operation. Thus, the examination of components of systems to detect signs of wear, and

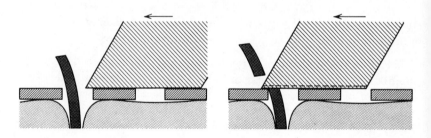

Fig. 5.1. Useful wear is illustrated by a self-sharpening shaver blade. As the cutting blade (top) slides back and forth, wear against its surface (broken line) preserves the cutting edge, which is kept in close contact with the opposite surface by spring loading.

Fig. 5.2. Rodent's tooth has hard enamel (heavy line) along the outer surface and softer dentine inside. The result is that wear progresses more rapidly on the inner side, leaving a hard cutting edge of enamel that tends to preserve the tooth's pointed shape.

especially, signs of wear in the wrong place, is an important part of failure analysis.

Familiar examples are the inspection of shoe soles and heels to see if their wearer is walking properly, and similarly, the inspection of wear in car tires to see if the wheels are straight.

5.3 Types of Wear

Modern research has established that there are four main forms of wear besides a few marginal processes which are often classified as forms of wear. Each wear process obeys its own laws and, to confuse matters, on many occasions one of the modes of wear acts in such a way as to affect the others. It then becomes our task to disentangle a complex situation, and to find the primary cause of wear.

Before we describe the various forms of wear, we should point out that the terminology in this field is quite unsettled, and likely to remain so for some time, since nothing, apparently, is being done to produce standardization. The terminology we have used is that of Burwell (1958), which seems to be simple and logical, and to seek out the primary cause of each form of wear.

Another approach is to examine the surfaces of the sliding specimens, which makes it possible to determine the final stage which must have been reached before wear occurred. Thus, if a clean smooth copper flat surface is slid on a similarly clean smooth steel surface, there is a transfer of particles from each surface to the other, and a scratching of each surface by the other. If the type of wear is judged by an inspection of the surfaces, the decision (wrong in my opinion) will be abrasive wear, because the formation of scratches is a sign of abrasive action. In reality, this is an example of adhesive wear, because the real cause of the particles (and of the scratches), is the transfer of particles from one surface to another by adhesive action.

A third approach is to judge the type of wear by its engineering consequences; thus, "light," "beneficial," wear if it helps the surfaces to run in properly, "severe" wear if in the opinion of the observer the wear is too rapid, "galling" if the surfaces become very rough and irregular in appearance, "seizing" if the motor driving the system stalls. This classification tells next to nothing about the mechanism of wear.

In the sections that follow, we shall describe and illustrate the main forms of wear. Detailed discussions of the equations which govern the rates of wear are left to later chapters.

Adhesive wear. This is the form of wear which occurs when two smooth bodies are slid over each other, and fragments are pulled off one surface to adhere to the other. Later, these fragments may come off the surface on which they are formed and be transferred back to the original surface, or else form loose wear particles.

Adhesive wear arises from the strong adhesive forces set up whenever atoms come into intimate contact. During sliding, a small patch on one of the surfaces comes into contact with a similar patch on the

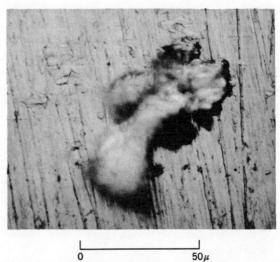

0   50μ

Fig. 5.3. Adhesive wear of a copper particle on a steel surface. Part of the copper particle is protruding so far that it is quite out of focus.

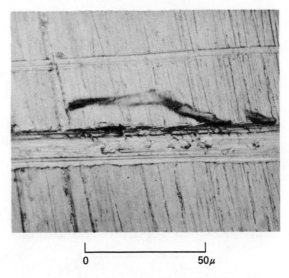

L_____J
0   50μ

Fig. 5.4. Abrasive wear of a steel surface by emery paper. A chip has been
produced and is adhering next to the track formed by an abrasive grain.

other surface, and there is a probability, small but finite, that when
this contact is broken the break will occur not at the original interface,
but within one of the materials. In consequence, a transferred fragment will be formed. A typical example of adhesive wear is shown in
Fig. 5.3.

Abrasive wear. This is the form of wear which occurs when a
rough hard surface, or a soft surface containing hard particles, slides
on a softer surface, and ploughs a series of grooves in it (Fig. 5.4).
The material from the grooves is displaced in the form of wear particles,
generally loose ones.

Corrosive wear. This form of wear occurs when sliding takes
place in a corrosive environment. In the absence of sliding, the
products of the corrosion would form a film on the surfaces, which
would tend to slow down or even arrest the corrosion, but the sliding
action wears the film away, so that the corrosive attack can continue.
It is not easy to find a good illustration of corrosive wear, but an
example is presented as Fig. 5.5.

Surface fatigue wear. This form of wear is observed during
repeated sliding or rolling over a track. The repeated loading and
unloading cycles to which the materials are exposed may induce the

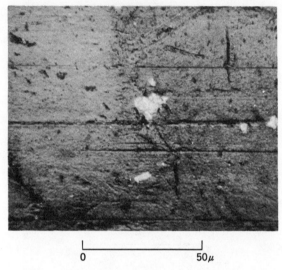

0   50μ

Fig. 5.5. Corrosive wear of boron carbide after sliding against steel at 1000°C. Note the smooth, rounded appearance of the surface features. [The light patches are steel fragments, formed as result of adhesive wear.]

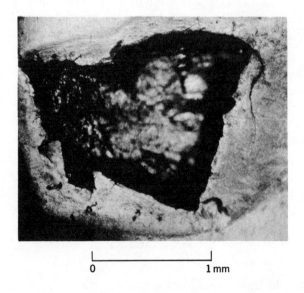

0   1 mm

Fig. 5.6. Surface fatigue wear of a steel ball. The pit is much larger than the surface features shown in Figs. 5.3 to 5.5 (note different magnifications).

formation of surface or subsurface cracks, which eventually will result in the break-up of the surface with the formation of large fragments, leaving large pits in the surface (Fig. 5.6). An analogous form of wear is shown by brittle materials, which break up in the form of large fragments.

5.4 Relative Importance of the Forms of Wear

In view of the fact that there are no less than four forms of wear, it may seem remarkable that materials in sliding contact enjoy any kind of useful life whatever. It should be realized, however, that all but one of the forms of wear can be made to disappear without very great difficulty, and even that can be greatly minimized.

Thus abrasive wear occurs only when a hard, rough surface is present, or when hard abrasive grains are present between two softer sliding surfaces. If we make sure that the hard surfaces in our system are very smooth, and arrange that no abrasive grains get into the system, abrasive wear can be eliminated. Similarly, corrosive wear is prevented if we make sure that the sliding materials do not react chemically with the atmosphere or lubricant in which they operate.

Surface fatigue wear occurs only in systems where the same volume of matter at the sliding surface is stressed and unstressed a large number of times, and hence it does not occur in a system in which other forms of wear are occurring, since these other forms of wear will continuously remove surface material before it has a chance to become fatigued. Only in cases of rolling contact (ball bearings or gears), in which case other forms of wear are very low, does fatigue wear occur. The analogous brittle fracture form of wear only occurs with brittle materials. But these are exceptional situations.

By a process of elimination, we have arrived at adhesive wear as being the most common, least preventable form of wear. As far as is known, this form of wear is universal in all mechanical systems in which two solids slide in contact with each other. It cannot be eliminated, only reduced.

Although adhesive wear is the most universal form of wear, it is not necessarily the most dangerous, since adhesive wear rates are usually fairly low. It is the unexpected occurrence of the other forms of wear, for example abrasive wear, which often produces unexpectedly high wear rates, and early failure of the mechanism.

The examination of a "failed" sliding member, to determine the type of wear responsible. is often a complex process. For details, the reader is referred to Burwell (1951); Furman, Tobin, and Strauss

(1957); Kaufman and Walp (1953); Love (1957); Ronan, Furman, and Bugbee (1958); Snook (1953); and Sprague and Dundy (1959).

5.5 Other Forms of Wear

In this section we shall discuss fretting, cavitation, and erosion, the other phenomena which are sometimes classified as types of wear. As regards fretting, it seems that this is not a primary form of wear, but a phenomenon which occurs when other wear mechanisms act together under oscillatory sliding conditions. Whether erosion or cavitation are admitted as forms of wear depends on whether damage by impacting particles or by the sudden boiling of a liquid are accepted as falling within the category of "mechanical action." In my opinion this is a very moot point.

Fretting. This form of wear arises when contacting surfaces undergo oscillatory tangential displacement of small amplitude. A typical example would be a splined out-of-line shaft coupling, in which the steel teeth undergo one small tangential to and fro movement per shaft revolution. As a result of the movement, adhering steel particles are produced (adhesive wear), and these oxidize (corrode) to Fe_2O_3. This is abrasive, and then causes abrasive wear of the surfaces. To sum up, this is a case where adhesive, corrosive, and abrasive forms of wear are all present. A useful review is that of Barnett (1955).

In former days, this form of wear was generally referred to as fretting corrosion (c.f. Halliday and Hirst, 1956), because it was felt that the formation of an abrasive oxide was the key step in causing fretting. Fretting has been observed, however, with materials which do not oxidize, such as cupric oxide (Godfrey and Bailey, 1954), so that this nomenclature is best abandoned.

Fretting is often a surprising type of wear because the motion which produces it is so small (per cycle) that it may be difficult to anticipate the overall large volume of wear debris that is produced. The wear is made especially large because of a peculiarity of the geometry. If the amplitude of vibration is small, it may be difficult for a lubricant to work its way into the interface, and the wear debris carries away any lubricant that was there initially.

It is difficult to suggest general ways of overcoming fretting, because changing any of the main variables may be either good or bad, and hence unpredictable. Thus if we increase the normal load, this is good if it prevents slip at the interface, but bad if the interfacial slip remains the same so that all the wear rates increase in proportion. If we increase the amplitude of vibration, this is good if it allows fresh lubricant to work its way into the interface, but bad if it just increases the amount of sliding action.

Fretting can be eliminated by eliminating slip at the interface. If there has to be some slip, solid film lubricants like a molybdenum disulfide-resin combination, or a soft metal like cadmium, are helpful. Hard coatings like chrome plate are generally bad, as they merely enable the fourth form of wear—surface fatigue wear—to come into the picture!

Erosion. The damage produced by sharp particles impinging an object is closely analogous to that produced by abrasion. The main difference is that in erosion the surface roughness produced may become relatively greater, because an impinging particle may readily remove material from a low point on the surface.

For details of the erosion process, the reader is referred to reviews by Finnie (1960) and Bitter (1963).

Cavitation. When a portion of a liquid is under tensile stresses, it may boil. Later, the bubble may collapse suddenly, producing a mechanical shock. A nearby solid surface may be damaged by this shock, leading to the removal of a particle. This process is cavitation.

Cavitation is closely akin to surface fatigue wear, and materials that are resistant to surface fatigue wear, namely hard but not brittle substances, are resistant to cavitation. Resistance to corrosion attack by the liquid, however, is an additional requirement for cavitation resistance! For a discussion of materials resistant to cavitation damage, see Rheingans (1957).

5.6 The Measurement of Wear

The most common way of studying wear consists of before and after examination of the sliding materials, any difference in the materials being attributed to wear. The detection of wear generally uses one or another of the techniques of weighing, of mechanical gaging, or of optical examination of surface features. We proceed to discuss these techniques in turn, especially in terms of their resolution, or least amount of wear which can be detected.

The weighing method. This is usually the simplest way of detecting wear, since it at once gives the total amount of wear in the form of a single number (of course, many times we are interested in the distribution of wear over the sliding surface, in which case the

weighing method is inadequate).   To carry out a weighing, it is necessary to remove from the sliding mechanism the component to be
examined, to clean it carefully (solvents like trichloroethylene or
acetone are generally used with metals), and then to carry out the
weighing on a chemical balance.

The limit of resolution of the weighing method is generally around
10^{-4} gm. It is set by three factors, namely: our inability to clean
materials consistently enough, so that the residues left on them produce
a weight uncertainty; the material transfer, unpredictable in direction,
which occurs at the points where our component is fastened into the
sliding mechanism; lastly by the limit of resolution of the typical chemical balance used for wear measurements.

The mechanical gaging method.   Typically, the micrometer
has a resolution limit of about 10^{-3} cm, which for a rider of surface
area 10^{-2} cm^2 allows us to measure down to 10^{-4} gm.   Usually, however, mechanical gaging is used on sliding components of considerable
size (e.g., automobile engine cylinders), and then the minimum amount
of wear which may be detected becomes much larger.

An alternative method of measuring wear, one which is of special
use when wear is confined to a narrow track, involves taking a profile
of the track with a profile meter (Section 3.4) and then estimating the
amount of material worn away.   For a track of length 3 cm, width
10^{-2} cm, and depth 10 microinches (all typical figures, see Fig. 5.7) we
may detect a weight loss of 10^{-5} gm.

Optical method.   There are a number of methods of measuring
wear using an optical technique.   One way is to make a small microhardness indentation in a surface, and to study how its size is reduced
during sliding (Fig. 5.8).   The horizontal limit of resolution of the

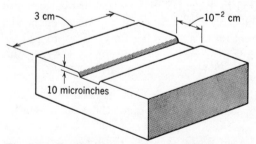

Fig. 5.7.   Profilometer method of measuring wear.

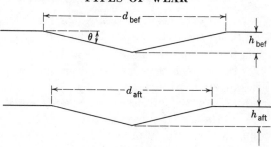

Fig. 5.8.   Indentation method of measuring wear.   Depth of wear $= h_{bef} - h_{aft} = (d_{bef} - d_{aft}) \tan \theta/2$.

optical method is about 10^{-4} cm, which, for an indentation of slope 1:5, becomes a depth limit of 10^{-5} cm.   Thus we may hope to measure wear with the same limitations as with the profile meter method considered earlier.

5.7   Measurement of Wear Using Radiotracers

The advent in the late 1940's of radioactive isotopes of the common engineering metals has had a profound effect on the study of wear. This has come about primarily because of the increased resolution in detecting wear, which the use of radiotracers makes possible.   Consequently, it has become possible to measure wear while it is occurring, rather than by before-and-after types of measurements.

Although a detailed discussion of radiotracer techniques would be out of place here (the reader is referred to Cook and Rabinowicz, 1963, and to Kohl, Zentner, and Lukens, 1961), we shall briefly review the main ways in which radiotracers have been applied to the wear problem.

Measurement of radioactive pick-up.   A radioactive material is slid over a nonradioactive surface, and the amount of radioactivity transferred to the inert surface is measured, either using a counter to give the total amount of wear, or else using a piece of photographic film in contact with the film to give the distribution of the transferred particles (see Fig. 6.6).   When a counter is used, as little as 10^{-9} gm of transfer can be readily detected, whereas photographic film brings the limit of detection down to 10^{-12} gm.

Measurement of nonadherent wear debris.   When a mechanism such as an engine or a pump is operated in the presence of a circulating lubricant, it is possible to measure the amount of wear debris in the lubricant by making one or more sliding members radioactive, and then monitoring the lubricant for radioactivity by means of a counter. If the lubricant is recirculated, we measure the build-up of wear particles in the lubricant, and thus get an integrated value of wear. Alternatively, if the lubricant is passed through only once, then a record is obtained of the wear as a function of time.

This technique is very widely used in the wear testing of engines, and has increased to an enormous extent the effectiveness of such testing by reducing the time required for one test from a period of several weeks to a period of a few minutes.

Specialized testing methods. Radiotracer techniques are so versatile that we may carry out a number of unusual and refined experiments with them. Thus we may take a sliding component, make different regions of it radioactive in different ways (for example one β-emitting and one γ-emitting, or two isotopes emitting γ-rays of different energies) and then, carefully monitoring the wear debris, compare the wear from the different areas (Abowd, 1958). Or else we may study the whole dynamics of the wear process by sliding a radioactive wear specimen on a nonradioactive surface to form a layer of radioactive debris on the latter, then replace the radioactive specimen by a non-radioactive one, continue sliding, and see how quickly the radioactive debris is replaced on the nonradioactive surface (Kerridge, 1955; Steijn, 1959).

Measurement of the different forms of wear. In the foregoing discussion we have been concerned mainly with the adhesive form of wear. There have been a number of radiotracer studies of abrasive wear, however, to determine, for example, how many abrasive particles adhere to the surface being abraded (Williams, 1957; Vainshtein and Prondzinskii 1962).

In studying corrosive wear we may either make the surface being corroded radioactive and measure the corrosive liquid for the presence of radioactive material, or else radioactivate some component of the corrosive medium and then test for corrosion product on the sliding surface.

5.8 When to Use Radiotracer Techniques

Radiotracer techniques are generally used for two types of studies:

I. When the extreme resolution associated with radioactivity is needed.

II. When the tracing characteristics of these techniques are needed.

We have sufficiently discussed the sensitivity advantage of radiotracers. Suffice it to say that, when the amount of wear is large (for example, when studying abrasive wear), the extreme resolution of radioactivity can become something of an embarrassment, and overload Geiger counters, etc. Furthermore, weighing methods are capable of greater accuracy, speed, and simplicity.

The tracing property involved in the use of radioisotopes is most valuable in the exploratory stages of an investigation. It enables us to find out what the mechanism of wear is, and to locate where it is occurring. Thereafter, it is often possible to discontinue the use of radiotracers and to carry out wear tests with other methods.

References

Abowd, R. G. (1958), Chrome Face vs. Iron Side Wear—An Analysis of some Radioactive Piston-Ring Wear Studies, *Trans. Am. Soc. Lubrication Eng.*, **1**, 91–95.

Barnett, R. S. (1955), Fretting and Fretting Corrosion, *Lubrication*, **41**, 85–96.

Bitter, J. G. A. (1963), A Study of Erosion Phenomena, *Wear*, **6**, 5–21, 169–190.

Burwell, J. T. (1951), Wear Tests and Service Performance, pp. 88–140 of *Interpretation of Tests and Correlation with Service*, American Society for Metals, Cleveland.

Burwell, J. T. (1957), Survey of Possible Wear Mechanisms, *Wear*, **1**, 119–141.

Cook, N. H., and E. Rabinowicz (1963), *Physical Measurement and Analysis*, Addison-Wesley, Reading, Mass.

Finnie, I. (1960), Erosion of Surfaces by Solid Particles, *Wear*, **3**, 87–103.

Furman, G. R., F. Tobin, and K. H. Strauss (1957), Abrasives and Wear, *Lubrication*, **43**, 13–24.

Godfrey, D., and J. M. Bailey (1954), Early Stages of Fretting of Copper, Iron and Steel, *Lubrication Engineering*, **10**, 155–159.

Halliday, J. S., and W. Hirst (1956), The Fretting Corrosion of Mild Steel, *Proc. Roy. Soc.*, **A 236**, 411–425.

Kaufman, H. N., and H. O. Walp (1953), *Interpreting Service Damage in Rolling Type Bearings*, American Society of Lubrication Engineers, Chicago.

Kerridge, M. (1955), Metal Transfer and the Wear Process, *Proc. Phys. Soc.* (*London*), **68 B**, 400–407.

Kohl, J., R. D. Zentner, and H. R. Lukens (1961), *Radioisotope Applications in Engineering*, Van Nostrand, Princeton, N.J.

Love, P. P. (1957), Diagnosis and Analysis of Plain Bearing Failures, *Wear*, **1**, 196–210.

Rabinowicz, E., and D. Tabor (1951), Metallic Transfer between Sliding Metals: an Autoradiographic Study, *Proc. Roy. Soc.*, **A 208**, 455–475.

Rheingans, Wm. J. (ed), (1957), *Cavitation Damage*, American Society of Mechanical Engineers, New York.

Ronan, R. J., G. R. Furman, and J. T. Bugbee (1958), Petroleum Laboratory Investigations, *Lubrication*, **44**, 29–44.

Snook, W. A. (1953), Automotive Engine Bearings, *Lubrication*, **39**, 61–76.

Sprague, H. G., and M. Dundy (1959), Analysis of Deposits, *Lubrication*, **45**, 1–12.

Steijn, R. P. (1959), Sliding Wear and Metal Transfer under Unlubricated Conditions, *Trans. Am. Soc. Mech. Eng.*, **D81**, 67–78.

Vainshtein, V. E., and A. M. Prondzinskii (1962), Use of Radioactive Tracers for Evaluation of the Ability of Bearing Materials to Absorb Abrasive Particles from the Lubricant, published in *Friction and Wear in Machinery*, translated by the A.S.M.E., New York, **15**, 35–44.

Williams, K. J. (1957), The Embedment of Abrasive in Lapped Surfaces, pp. 602–605 of *Proc. Conf. Lubrication and Wear*, Institution of Mechanical Engineers, London.

6

Adhesive Wear

6.1 Introduction

This, the most common form of wear, exists whenever one solid material is slid over the surface of another or is pressed against it. The removal of material takes the form of small particles which are usually transferred to the other surface, but which may come off in loose form. This difference in behavior of the particles is, of course, always of theoretical significance. As a practical matter, its importance depends on the sliding geometry. For example, if material is removed from an automobile tire sliding against a road surface, then, it does not matter (as far as the useful life of the tire is concerned) whether the fragments are loose or transferred to the road, since in either case they are lost from the tire. For a journal bearing, however, the transfer of a fragment from one surface to the other will often not be detrimental to the life of the bearing if at a later stage the fragment can transfer back to its original surface, whereas the formation of a loose fragment is permanent and will adversely affect the bearing life. We might generalize this distinction in the form that the formation of transferred fragments is often not permanent in a repeated-traverse sliding situation, but that, naturally, it is irreversible in a single-traverse situation.

6.2 Mechanism of Adhesive Wear

The tendency of contacting surfaces to adhere arises from the attractive forces which exist between the surface atoms of the two materials.

If two surfaces are brought together and then separated, either normally or tangentially, these attractive forces act in such a way as to attempt to pull material from one surface on to the other.   Whenever material is removed from its original surface in this way, an adhesive wear fragment is created.

The early experiments on adhesive wear were carried out with metals, and the process of adhesion was referred to as "welding." This was, in a sense, an unfortunate choice of word, since among metallurgists the term "welding" is usually confined to joints between metals, produced at high temperatures, and accompanied by the inter-diffusion and recrystallization of material near the original interface of the surface atoms of the two metals (Fig. 6.1).   By contrast, in the case of adhesive wear the temperatures at the regions of real contact may be quite low, and atomic interdiffusion and recrystallization may be absent.   The conditions at the interface during adhesive wear are quite similar, however, to those prevailing in the "cold welding" process, in which clean strips of metals such as aluminum are joined by being pressed together while their contacting area is deformed and stretched (see Chapter 9).   In any case, since the concept of "welding" cannot be readily applied to adhesive processes in nonmetals, which

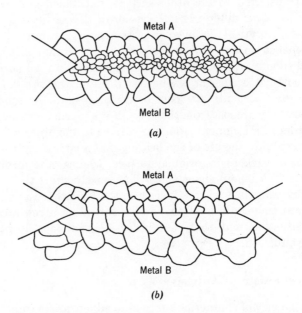

Fig. 6.1.   (a) A typical metallurgical weld.   (b) A typical adhesional joint.

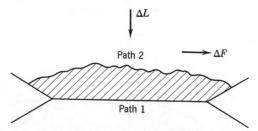

Fig. 6.2. A junction being sheared. If the shear strength of the junction is much bigger than the bulk strength of the top material, shear will take place along path 2 producing the fragment shaded.

latter materials do often show a marked tendency to undergo the transfer of material, it is preferable in all cases to use the term "adhesive wear" rather than "wear by welding."

How adhesive wear occurs is illustrated in Fig. 6.2, which shows in schematic form the interface of two contacting materials. A tangential displacement is imposed on one of the bodies. If the force required to break through the interface of the materials is larger than the force required to break through some continuous surface inside one of the materials, the break will occur along this latter surface, and a transferred wear particle will be produced.

Examination of Fig. 6.2 suggests that the formation of wear particles will be a rare event,[*] since the original interface of the contacting materials is liable to have the smallest cross-sectional area, and also, in view of the large number of misfits and vacancies likely to be present at such interfaces, the lowest strength. Hence the break during shearing is most likely to occur at the interface. Calculations based on experimental wear data suggest that in practice it is very seldom that as high a proportion as 5% of the junctions formed during sliding break in such a way as to produce a sizable wear particle, whereas values smaller than 0.01% are not uncommon.

The way in which wear particles form is graphically illustrated by the experiments of Green (1955) and of Greenwood and Tabor (1955, 1957) who used two-dimensional models of various metals and Plasticene to denote asperities, and then sheared the asperities. They

* Bikerman (1962) argues the opposite, namely that it must be a very rare event when a junction breaks precisely along its original interface. He is very likely right; but radiotracer techniques show that the very small clusters of atoms which find themselves on the wrong side of the shear plane after a typical junction breaks up contribute a negligible amount to the overall transfer.

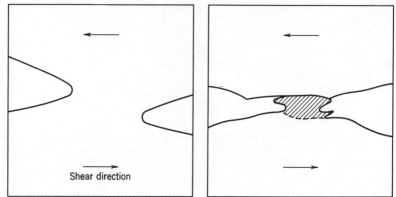

Shear direction

Fig. 6.3.   Experiment of Greenwood and Tabor (1957) with a soft, two-dimensional, copper model, showing formation of a fragment.

showed that, under some circumstances, especially when the plane of the junction was not parallel to the sliding direction, transferred particles could be formed, (Fig. 6.3).   This nonparallelism might occur because the surfaces were initially rough or else become rough during sliding.   Alternatively, if, as Feng (1952) postulates, the junction, while remaining parallel to the sliding direction, becomes roughened through slip effects, then again fragment formation might become more likely.

It should be emphasized, however, that it is by no means a necessary requirement for the formation of adhesive wear particles that the surfaces should be rough.   Even very smooth surfaces often give rise to adhesive wear, and in many cases the adhesive wear rate is independent of surface roughness (Fig. 6.4).

Consideration of the model of wear particle formation as shown in Fig. 6.2 suggests that all the breaks which did not take place at the interface would occur inside the softer material, this being by definition of lower mechanical strength than the harder material.   Consequently, we would have the situation that fragments of the softer material might be formed, but not fragments of the harder material. This is definitely not the case.   Although in most cases *more* fragments of the softer material are formed, and they are usually larger, too, it is a fact that in all cases which have been studied of the sliding or normal contact of two unlike materials, fragments of the hard material are also formed.   This suggests that, within the harder material, there are local regions of low strength.   If these coincide, at a junction, with

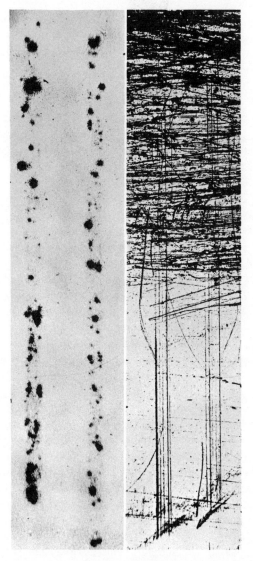

Fig. 6.4.   Micrograph and autoradiograph of a copper surface, part of which has a roughness of 1 microinch, the other part 20 microinches, after a radioactive copper rider had been slid over it.   Load 4 kg, speed 0.01 cm/sec, lubricant copper palmitate.   The wear seems independent of roughness.

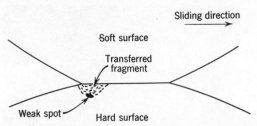

Fig. 6.5.   Schematic illustration of how a weak spot in hard surface leads to fragment formation.   Hard material fragments are usually small (smaller than the junction).

local regions of high strength of the softer material, the fragment formed will be of the harder material (Fig. 6.5).

There is a great paucity of data on the relative wear of two materials of widely differing hardness.   What little data exists suggests that if two materials differ in hardness by a ratio R, their wear rates will vary inversely as R^2.   But no matter how much we increase the hardness ratios of the two contacting materials it does not appear that we can ever reduce the wear of the harder material to zero.   Thus, even soft polymers like Teflon will remove quite sizable amounts of matter from metals as strong as a low-carbon steel (Rabinowicz and Shooter, 1952).

6.3   The Sizes and Shapes of Transferred Fragments

There has been little systematic work done in determining the sizes and shapes of transferred wear particles.   Most of our own work has been done using just one pair of metals, copper against a low-carbon steel.   This combination was chosen so that the wear fragments would be readily visible under the microscope because of their dissimilar colors, and as a further advantage both surfaces could be readily made radioactive in a nuclear pile.

In Fig. 6.6a, we show a typical wear track on a flat steel surface over which a copper hemispherically ended rider has passed, leaving a number of copper transferred wear fragments.   These particles were studied in a number of ways.   Thus, in a microscope with calibrated eye-piece, the length and width of each particle was measured, and also the height of the top point on each larger particle above the steel surface, using for this purpose the calibrated fine focusing adjustment of the microscope.

In addition, since the copper rider which produced these fragments had previously been made radioactive, it was possible to produce an autoradiograph by placing the steel surface against a photographic plate and later developing the plate (Fig. 6.6b). From the black impression produced by each fragment, it was possible to calculate the volume of each fragment (Rabinowicz, 1953). Since the data obtained in this study appear to have quite universal application, they will be reported in some detail.

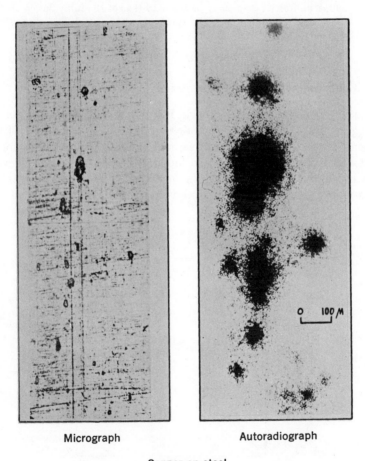

Micrograph   Autoradiograph

Copper on steel

Fig. 6.6. Micrograph and autoradiograph of an unlubricated steel surface, after radioactive copper rider had passed over it.

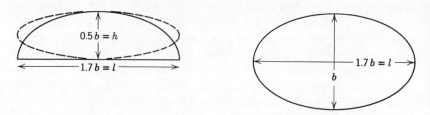

Fig. 6.7. (a) Side view of a typical fragment. In calculations we assume it to
be a semiellipsoid, but its shape may be closer to that of the full ellipsoid shown
by the dashed line. In either case, the volume is $\pi lbh/6$. (b) Top view of the
typical fragment. The constant of 1.7 is derived from Fig. 6.9.

6.4   The Shapes of Wear Fragments

The largest copper wear particle in Fig. 6.6, just above the center of
the figure, was found under the microscope to have a length l of 90
microns, a breadth b of 38 microns, and the height h of its topmost
point above the steel surface was found to be 20 microns.   Viewed
from above, the fragment resembles an ellipse; and it seems reasonable
to assume that the fragment approximates to the top half of an

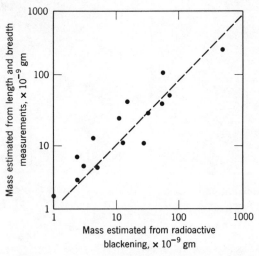

Fig. 6.8.   Two estimates of particle size agree well, thus confirming $h = b/2$
(approx.).

ellipsoid (Fig. 6.7). The mass of such a semiellipsoid is $\pi l b h/6$; and, in this case, this would work out at 3.2×10^{-7} gm. By an independent radiotracer technique, based on a determination of the area of the blackened circle in Fig. 6.6b, the mass of the particle was calculated at 4×10^{-7} gm, with a probable uncertainty of $\pm 30\%$. This is as close to the value obtained by direct measurement as we could have expected. For the smaller fragments in Fig. 6.6a, it was not possible to measure their height directly; but we can calculate their mass assuming that they all have the same shape so that their height is one-half their breadth, and compare this value with their mass as derived from the autoradiographs. These values are compared in Fig. 6.8, and it will be seen that the two estimates agree quite closely, suggesting that the height of all the fragments is indeed of the order of magnitude of one-half their breadth.

Next we may compare the other dimensions of the fragments by plotting their extension along the direction of sliding against their extension at right angles. Figure 6.9 shows that this ratio is fairly constant for all the particles, averaging 1.7. From the fact that the particles are elongated along the direction of sliding, we may deduce that during the contact of two asperities a factor must be present which elongates the area of contact along the sliding direction. This factor may be adhesion, which hinders or delays the breaking of the back end

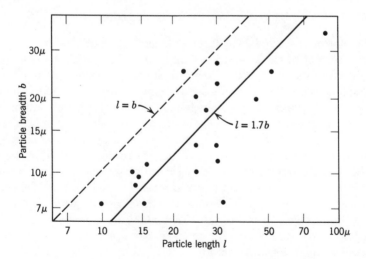

Fig. 6.9. Plot of length of particles (i.e., dimension along the sliding direction) versus their width (across sliding direction). The average particle is 1.7 times as long as it is wide.

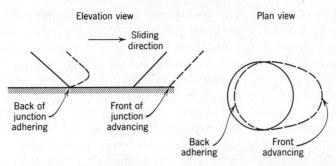

Fig. 6.10. Schematic view of junction to show effect of adhesion. Junction is assumed circular initially, but adhesion elongates it (and any particle produced by it).

of the junction while junction growth is taking place at the front end (Fig. 6.10).

In summary then, we may say that adhesive fragments appear to be semiellipsoids, of dimensions approximately $1.7 \times 1 \times 0.5$, the largest dimension being along the sliding direction and the smallest dimension at right angles to the surface. The fragment shape is substantially independent of the size of the fragments.

6.5   The Size Distribution of Wear Fragments

A plot of the number of fragments against their size, based on the measurement of the autoradiograph of which Fig. 6.6b is a small part, is shown in Fig. 6.11. The small fragments are seen to be much more numerous than the large ones. It is convenient to be able to quote an average particle size or an average particle mass for a distribution such as that shown in Fig. 6.11. The usual method of obtaining an average mass—namely, that of dividing the total mass by the total number of particles, is not available to us because the total number of particles is unknown, since most of the particles are very small. However, if we plot the per cent of the total transfer represented by particles of any mass as a function of particle mass, we get Fig. 6.12, which is obtained by multiplying each column in Fig. 6.11 by its average mass. From Fig. 6.12, we can define the average particle such that all heavier particles weigh as much as all lighter ones. In Fig. 6.12, this corresponds to finding the vertical line which has the area on its right equal to the area on its left.

If our average particle has an average shape, then we can say that its length and height will be 1.7 and 0.5 times its breadth. Hence, we

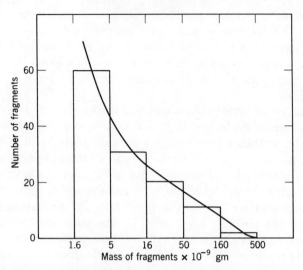

Fig. 6.11.   Histogram of wear fragments.

define the average dimension of a particle by the equation

$$m = \pi\rho \times 1.7b_a \times b_a \times \frac{0.5b_a}{6}$$

$$b_a = 1.32 \left(\frac{m}{\rho}\right)^{\frac{1}{3}} \qquad (6.1)$$

Values of the average dimension of the particles making up the dis-

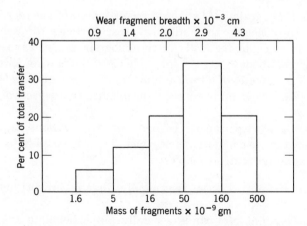

Fig. 6.12.   Relative importance of the various groups of fragments.

tribution of Fig. 6.12 are plotted on top of the figure. As will be seen, 80% of the total wear is made up of particles with an average dimension differing by less than a factor of two from that of the average particle. This is rather a small size range. It appears likely that all, or at any rate almost all, of the particles are produced by the same physical process.

It must be admitted that a different interpretation of the results is possible. Since the largest 10% of the particles differ in linear dimensions by more than a factor of four from the smallest 10%, the difference in volume and mass is by more than a factor of 64, or about two orders of magnitude. Dimensional analysis suggest that the numerical constants should be small for equations which connect physical quantities, and if we hypothesize an equation for the mass of a particle, then if all the particles are formed by the same process, not all the numerical constants could be small. This suggests that more than one process is operative. If we look at particle diameters, however, all these are within an order of magnitude, consequently an equation with small numerical constants could exist.

This then gives rise to the question whether the mass or the length is the primary, characteristic, dimension of a wear particle. We shall see later that it is the linear dimension which appears to be primary, since it enters directly into expressions for the wear particle size. Accordingly, we conclude that all the wear particles have nearly the same characteristic size, and hence may well be the product of the same mechanism.

6.6   Quantitative Laws of Adhesive Wear

As result of our detailed study of wear particles of one representative system, we conclude that adhesive wear particles for unlubricated copper on steel, under loads in the kilogram range, have a typical dimension of about 3×10^{-3} cm. This is of the same order of magnitude as the diameter of a typical junction of these materials (see Chapter 3). We now go on to consider the quantitative aspects of adhesive wear.

As result of experiments carried out with various unlubricated materials, the vast majority being metallic, it is possible to write the laws of adhesive wear as follows:

1. The amount of wear is generally directly proportional to the load L.

2. The amount of wear is generally proportional to the distance slid x.

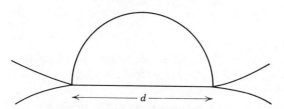

Fig. 6.13.   Hypothetical model of a hemispherical wear particle.

3. The amount of wear is generally inversely proportional to the hardness p of the surface being worn away.

Or, we can write the volume worn away in the form (Holm, 1946)

$$V = \frac{cLx}{p} \tag{6.2}$$

where c is a nondimensional constant dependent on the materials in contact and their exact degree of cleanliness.

The real evidence for this equation is rather mixed, typical being some tests in which the formation of adhesive particles was studied (Rabinowicz and Tabor, 1951), other experiments in which poorly lubricated, loose particles were measured (Burwell and Strang, 1952), etc.   Many investigators have found that eq. 6.2 is not always perfectly obeyed, but in almost all cases it represents the experimental data reasonably well.

Archard (1953) has presented a very plausible model of the sliding process, which enables eq. 6.2 to be derived quite simply, and which allows us to attach a definite meaning to the constant c in eq. 6.2. Archard assumes that each time two asperities come into contact to form a junction, there is a constant probability k that an adhesive fragment will be formed.   Each fragment is assumed to be a hemisphere of diameter equal to the junction diameter (Fig. 6.13).

If now, we consider the case of two bodies sliding under an applied load L, and call the flow pressure of the softer of the metals p; then, the real area of contact will be given by

$$L = p \cdot A \tag{6.3}$$

If it is assumed that all the junctions are of the same size, circles of diameter d, and hence of area $\pi d^2/4$, then the total number n present at any instant will be given by

$$A = n \cdot \frac{\pi d^2}{4}$$

Hence
$$n = \frac{4A}{\pi d^2} = \frac{4L}{\pi p d^2} \tag{6.4}$$

Each junction may be assumed to remain in existence during a sliding distance equal to d, after which it is broken and its load-carrying capacity is taken up by a new junction. (Actually the load-displacement function is more complicated, as Fig. 6.14 shows, but the assumption of an effective working distance of d is a good approximation).

Making the assumption of an effective working distance of d, each junction, per centimeter of sliding, must be replenished a total of $1/d$ times, and thus the total number N of junctions formed per centimeter is given by

$$N = \frac{n}{d} = \frac{4L}{\pi p d^3} \tag{6.5}$$

The probability that any junction leads to the formation of a transferred fragment has been postulated to be equal to k, and, on the assumption that such a fragment is a hemisphere of diameter d, the volume, $\delta V/\delta x$, of wear per centimeter of sliding, is given by the relation

$$\frac{\delta V}{\delta x} = \frac{k \cdot N \cdot \pi d^3}{12} = \frac{kL}{3p} \tag{6.6}$$

The volume of transferred fragments formed in sliding through a distance x, then becomes

$$V = \frac{kLx}{3p} \tag{6.7}$$

This may be considered the fundamental law of adhesive wear, and

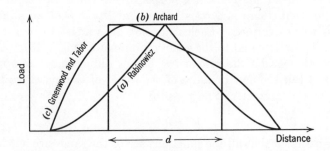

Fig. 6.14. Load-displacement functions of a junction. (a) As calculated by Rabinowicz (1951). (b) As assumed by Archard (1953). (c) As measured, using an aluminum model, by Greenwood and Tabor (1955). The area under each curve, representing the total load-distance carried by each junction, is about the same.

Table 6.1. Wear Constant k of Various Sliding Combinations

Combination	Wear Constant k
Zinc on zinc	160×10^{-3}
Low carbon steel on low carbon steel	45
Copper on copper	32
Stainless steel on stainless steel	21
Copper (on low carbon steel)	1.5
Low carbon steel (on copper)	0.5
Bakelite on bakelite	0.02

k the coefficient of wear. Like the coefficient of friction, k is dimensionless. It will be seen that eq. 6.7 is identical in form with eq. 6.2, the only difference being that $k/3$ has replaced the arbitrary constant c.

One of the features of this calculation is that the junction diameter d does not enter into the final expression for the wear volume, and Archard shows that eq. 6.7 applies even if the junctions and the fragments derived from them cover a range of size, as is indeed the case. All that it is necessary to postulate is that the fragment and junction diameters are always equal, and that the probability of forming a fragment is independent of the size of the junction. The factor three which somewhat mysteriously appears in the denominator is a shape factor, applicable in this case to the assumed circular junctions and hemispherical fragments. If we assumed square junctions and cubical fragments, the corresponding factor would be 1, whereas other constants would apply for fragments of other shapes. For particles measured in Section 6.5 as having the shape $1.7 \times 1 \times 0.5$, the shape factor to be applied in eq. 6.7 is again three, because each junction is in contact for a distance 1.7 times as great as when hemispherical particles are formed, and thus there are fewer junctions in this ratio than eq. 6.5 shows. Each fragment, however, is 1.7 times as large as the hemispherical one, so these quantities cancel out.

The only important requirement for eq. 6.2 to apply is that the volume of the fragment should be proportional to the cube of the junction diameter. This requirement appears to be generally met in practice.

Besides confirming that eq. 6.7 agrees with the laws of adhesive wear as enunciated at the beginning of this section, we can apply an additional test, based on the fact that k has been defined as a probability, and thus cannot exceed 1. Table 6.1 shows typical values of k, and it will be seen that k does in fact always remain well below 0.5. A much more extensive collection of data, based on all the values of k

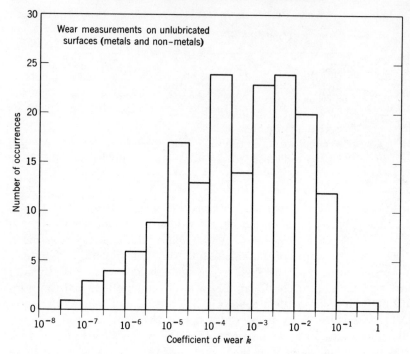

Fig. 6.15. Histogram of 172 values of the wear coefficient k, obtained with unlubricated surfaces. Values of k above 0.1 are very rare.

which I have measured, all the values of k which are readily computed from data given in the proceedings of the Conference on Lubrication and Wear (1957), and all the data given in the Transactions of the American Society of Lubrication Engineers (1958 to 1963), are shown in Fig. 6.15. Of the 172 data points, none is above 1. Figure 6.15 suggests that the probability of forming an adhesive wear particle is, in most cases, quite low.

6.7 Alternative Forms of the Wear Equation

It is possible to rewrite eq. 6.7 in a number of equivalent ways. First, we write V as the product of the average depth h worn away and the apparent area of contact A_a to obtain

$$h = \frac{kLx}{3pA_a} \tag{6.8}$$

Next, A_r, the real area of contact, may be substituted for L/p. This produces

$$h = \frac{k \cdot x \cdot A_r}{3A_a} \tag{6.9}$$

This form of the equation shows up clearly the nondimensioned nature of k. The distance h is proportional to the distance $x/3$, and to the ratio (A_r/A_a), so that the constant of proportionality k must be a pure number.

In the special case of a small rider loaded to the limit, so that plastic flow is imminent, the real and apparent areas become equal, and this simplifies down to

$$h = \frac{k \cdot x}{3} \tag{6.10}$$

This relation has an especially simple meaning. The velocity at which the surface of the rider "travels" into the other surface as result of its wearing away is equal to $k/3$ times the sliding velocity (Fig. 6.16).

Alternatively, we may start with (6.7) and substitute A_r, the real area of contact, for L/p. This gives

$$V = \frac{kA_rx}{3} \tag{6.11}$$

This equation is of importance to sliding systems whose electrical resistance must be kept below some specified value, and, therefore, whose value of A_r must be kept at or above some specified value. In this case, the wear rate depends only on k and is independent of the hardness and load except insofar as these parameters determine the wear constant k.

For example, if for a certain metal the wear constant k is the same for the metal in the annealed or hardened form, and for purposes of

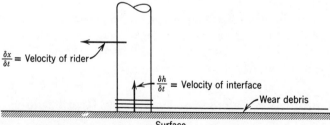

Fig. 6.16. For the rider loaded to the limit, the velocity of the interface into the rider is $(k/3)$ times the velocity of the rider along the surface.

electric current carrying capacity a certain value of A_r must be maintained, then it does not matter whether the metal is used in a soft or hard form, since the wear rate for constant A_r will be the same for both. The friction force, however, will be smaller when the softer metal is used, since sA_r ($= F$) will then be less. The author has found it difficult to convince others of the validity of this simple argument.

6.8   The Equilibrium Distribution of Transfer Fragments

In the previous section we have considered the initial transfer of material from one surface to the other, without concerning ourselves with other transfer and back-transfer processes of the same type which may be simultaneously occurring. As will later become apparent, these other processes may be ignored only for the case of a rider of small area sliding on a large surface of another material in such a way that the rider always traverses fresh regions of the other surface. For preference, the larger surface should show a smaller tendency to wear. In fact, most of the data of Table 6.1 were obtained under these conditions. In the general case, however, the wear process is considerably more complicated, because, during sliding, fragments are continually torn off each surface, transferred to the other, and later retransferred. In this section we propose, after making simplifying assumptions, to calculate the equilibrium configuration and the rate at which it is attained, and to compare the calculations with experimental findings.

Arguing intuitively we might imagine that, after sliding had continued for a very long time, the two materials had become so thoroughly intermingled that the surface of each specimen consisted of the same proportion of the two constituents. Experimental tests suggest, however, that this does not often occur when sliding takes place in air, although the phenomenon is occasionally observed. Instead, it is usually found that each surface still consists largely of its own bulk material, but with a small fraction covered by fragments from the other surface.

The choice between the two possible terminal states is determined by the tightness with which the transferred fragments are held on the other surface, and three separate calculations are necessary to cover the three possible situations.

6.9   Equilibrium Calculation for Loosely Held Fragments

We shall assume that material 1 is sliding on material 2 of similar hardness, that a fraction (a_1) of material 1 and (a_2) of material 2 are

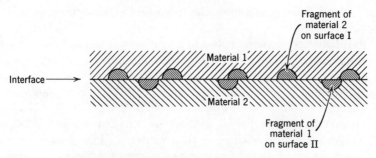

Fig. 6.17.   Schematic illustration of equilibrium of the transfer process.

covered by fragments of the other material, and that all the fragments, both of materials 1 and 2, are of the same size and shape (Fig. 6.17). Further, we define p as the probability, per contact, of transfer from material 1 to material 1, q as the probability per contact of transfer from material 2 to material 2, r as the probability per contact of transfer from material 1 to material 2, and s as the probability per contact of transfer from material 2 to material 1.

The rate at which fragments of material 1 arrive at surface II is equal to the total number (N) of junctions formed, multiplied by the fraction of surface I that is material 1, $(1 - a_1)$, the fraction of surface II that is material 2, $(1 - a_2)$, and the probability that a contact will produce a fragment, (r).   Similarly, the rate at which fragments of material 1 leave the surface II equals N multiplied by the concentration of material 1 in the surface II, (a_2), the concentration of material 1 in the surface I, namely $(1 - a_1)$, and the appropriate probability factor (p).   Hence, for equilibrium we write

$$N(1 - a_1)(1 - a_2)r = N(a_2)(1 - a_1)p \qquad (6.12)$$

and hence

$$a_2 = \frac{r}{p + r} \qquad (6.13)$$

Similarly, by examining the flux of material 2 fragments in surface I, we get

$$a_1 = \frac{s}{q + s} \qquad (6.14)$$

It should be noted that, in deriving these equations, we have assumed that transferred fragments are not held too tightly to the other metal and are unable themselves to pull out any further fragments.   The case where fragments induce the formation of more fragments is discussed later.

In calculating the constants p to s we must use transfer data obtained over small sliding distances, before the contamination of either surface by fragments from the other has become severe. For the case of copper sliding on steel, the wear constants as given in Table 6.1 are $p = 320$, $q = 450$, $r = 15$, and $s = 5$, all in units of 10^{-4}. Hence, we calculate the values for a_2 and a_1 as 4.5 and 1.1% respectively. Although the approximations in the calculations have been severe, it is believed that the values of a_1 and a_2 are correct, at least to within one order of magnitude.

Table 6.2 shows calculation of a for the foregoing combinations of materials and other typical sliding materials.

According to eqs. 6.13 and 6.14, the equilibrium configuration depends only on the wear constants p to s, and, insofar as these are almost independent of load, speed, and surface geometry, so is the equilibrium. Some experiments by Kerridge (1955) in which a soft steel rider was slid on a hard steel cylinder, confirm in a striking way the fact that a_1 does not depend on the applied load. Using a system where material 1 was soft steel and material 2 was a tool steel, he showed that when the load was changed by a factor of 10, the weight of fragments adhering in equilibrium to the cylinder changed by less than a factor of 30%. His data also provided a direct test of eq. 6.14. The area of his sliding surface was 4 cm^2; the volume of transfer was 10^{-4} cc. Assuming the diameter of a fragment to be 10^{-3} cm (a reasonable value) this gives $a_1 = 2.5\%$. From his data we can estimate s as being 5×10^{-4}. As above, q may be taken to be

Table 6.2. **Equilibrium Concentration of Transfer Fragments of Various Metal Combinations**

Fragments	Surface	Equilibrium Concentration Per Cent
Platinum	Silver	0.3
Cadmium	Steel	0.6
Steel	Copper	1.1
Platinum	Steel	3.7
Steel	Titanium	4.3
Copper	Steel	4.5
Titanium	Steel	29.0

Table 6.3.   Measured Equilibrium Concentration.
Cu-Be Fragments

Surface	Concentration	Surface	Concentration
Chromium	0.6%	Silver	4.4%
Lead	0.8	Nickel	5.1
Tin	0.9	Tin	7.6
Aluminum	2.0	Copper—	
Cadmium	2.9	Beryllium	48
Zinc	4.3	Phosphor bronze	103

450×10^{-4}.   Thus, from eq. 6.14 we find $a_1 = 1.1\%$.   In view of all the uncertainties, this seems as close to the actual value of 2.5% as we could reasonably expect.

The most extensive experimental work appears to be that of Sakmann, Burwell, and Irvine (1944) who slid various small metal riders on a radioactive copper-beryllium alloy, and measured the transfer of activity to the riders.   Table 6.3 is derived from the experimental values presented in Table VII of their paper.   The results are of the same order of magnitude as those shown in Table 6.2.

6.10   Equilibrium Calculation for Tightly Held Fragments

We now turn to the case of fragments that are held so tightly that they can pull off other fragments on to themselves.   This introduces a new phenomenon into the eqs. 6.12 to 6.14.

Referring to Fig. 6.1: if the fragments of material 1 on surface II can pull further fragments of material 1 to surface II, we must add a term $N(a_2)(1 - a_1)p$ to the left-hand side of eq. 6.12.   If the fragments of material 2 on surface I can pull fragments of material 1 off surface II, we add a term $N(a_2)(a_1)r$ to the right-hand side.   Thus we obtain

$$N(1 - a_1)(1 - a_2)r + N(a_2)(1 - a_1)p$$
$$= N(a_2)(1 - a_1)p + N(a_1)(a_2)r \quad (6.15)$$

or

$$a_1 + a_2 = 1 \quad (6.16)$$

Clearly the same relation between a_1 and a_2 will be obtained by considering the fragments of material 2, and hence a_1 and a_2 cannot be determined separately.   It is clear, however, that at least one of them must be $\frac{1}{2}$ or above.   In practice, one of them is usually 1 and the other zero, the choice being determined partly by chance and partly by surface geometry. As we shall show later, when we slide a small rider on a large flat surface, the initial concentration of fragments will normally be larger on the rider, so this is more likely to be the surface that is completely covered by fragments of the other. A number of such cases are reported in the literature, for example, platinum on silver, and copper on silver (Bowden, Leben, and Tabor, 1939).

In transfer between specimens of the same size, shape, and material, we see that if we draw a plane at the surface of one of the specimens (Fig. 6.18) such that the volume of specimen I to the left of the plane is the same as the volume of specimen I terminated by its actual surface, then each time a fragment is transferred to surface I, the plane moves a small distance to the right; each time a fragment is transferred to surface II, the plane moves correspondingly to the left. Wear being a random phenomenon, the position of the plane varies in a random fashion. The problem of finding the position of the plane under these random disturbances is the same as discussed by Einstein (1905) for the Brownian movement of particles; and the result is that, in general, the plane is distant from its starting position by an amount which varies as (time)$^{1/2}$. Thus, after a long period of sliding it is more probable than not in the line of demarcation will have moved into one of the specimens, so that one out of a_1 and a_2 is zero and the other is 1.

These considerations sometimes apply even when the specimens are not symmetrical. Figure 6.19 shows that when we slid a radioactive copper rider on a flat copper surface, the metal transfer to the flat surface is spasmodic. The autoradiograph consists of a series of black lines, corresponding to regions where the transfer is into the bottom plate, and blank regions when the top rider is covered by fragments of the bottom surface ($a = 1$) and no transfer is observed. These cor-

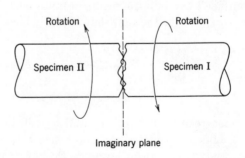

Fig. 6.18. The symmetrical wear problem.

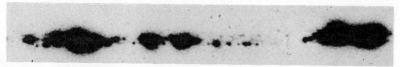

Fig. 6.19. Autoradiograph produced after sliding radioactive copper rider on an unlubricated copper surface. Load 2 kg. Magnification ×4.

respond to the excursion of the plane into the rider and the flat surface, respectively.

6.11 Equilibrium Calculation when One Set of Fragments is Held Tightly, the Other Loosely

This may be considered the intermediate step between the stages discussed in Sections 6.9 and 6.10.   It generally arises when one of the materials is much harder than the other.   Each of the two types of fragments is held on by the same adhesive attraction, that attributable to the material 1—material 2 interaction, and this may be "large" in comparison with the strength of the weaker material (material 1) but "small" in comparison with the strength of the harder material 2. If particles of material 2 on adhering to material 1 cannot pull particles off surface 1, but the particles of material 1 can pull off more particles, we use eq. 6.15 for one surface, but only three terms of the corresponding equation for the other surface.   This latter relation would then be

$$N(1 - a_2)(1 - a_1)s = Na_1(1 - a_2)q + Na_2a_1s \qquad (6.17)$$

Equation 6.17 simplifies to

$$(1 - a_1 - a_2)s = a_1(1 - a_2)q \qquad (6.18)$$

which may be combined with eq. 6.16 to yield

$$a_1 = 0$$

$$a_2 = 1 \qquad (6.19)$$

Thus the result of this type of interaction is that the hard surface is completely covered by fragments of the soft material, but that no fragments of the hard material are to be found on the soft surface. This final state is similar to that discussed in Section 6.10.   There we found that either surface might become completely covered by fragments of the other.   Now we find that, for unlike materials of dissimilar hardness, it is the harder surface which is likely to become covered by fragments of the softer one, but not the reverse.   Practical experience agrees very well with this calculation.

6.12   Initial Transfer Rates–Surfaces Not in Equilibrium

The foregoing discussion has been devoted to finding the equilibrium state of sliding surfaces.   Another question of some importance is the way that equilibrium is reached, and specifically, the events that occur as sliding of the two surfaces is first initiated.   If the rate of formation of junctions is written as dN/dt, the rate of formation of fragments on surface 2 will be $(r \times dN/dt)$ whereas fragments will form on surface 1 at the rate $(s \times dN/dt)$.   In a situation where material 1 and material 2 have similar strength, r and s will be of the same order of magnitude, and thus the rates of transfer will be of the same order of magnitude.

It follows that, if one of the surfaces is much smaller than the other (i.e., if its apparent area of contact A_a is much smaller), this surface will become covered by fragments of the other at a much more rapid rate.   For many systems, it is found that as soon as about 10% of the surface is covered by fragments of the other, these fragments are close enough to each other that they can cooperate to transfer further fragments to the surface to which they are adhering, so that, once the 10% coverage of a surface is reached, that surface effectively moves from the "fragments loosely held" to the "fragments tightly held" category, as defined in Sections 6.9 and 6.10.   Thus, since the smaller surface will reach 10% coverage earlier, it will be the smaller surface that is covered by fragments of the other.   This is seen in Fig. 6.20, which shows photomicrographs for a titanium rider on a titanium flat, a titanium rider on a steel flat, and a steel rider on a titanium flat. The steel rider on a titanium flat quickly produces a titanium-on-titanium situation, whereas the titanium rider on a steel flat quickly produces a steel-on-steel situation.   Where the riders are, as in this case, hemispherically ended rods which make contact over a very small area, this complete coverage is produced in a small sliding distance, which may be as little as 0.2 cm.

For the system steel-titanium, this difference in rate of coverage takes on great practical importance, since the system steel-on-steel is readily lubricated, whereas titanium-on-titanium can be lubricated only with difficulty, and then never well.   These characteristics carry over to the titanium-on-steel and the steel-on-titanium systems respectively.   Thus a steel rider sliding on a titanium flat lubricated by palmitic acid in cetane gives a friction of 0.48 (the same value as for titanium on titanium), but a titanium rider on a steel surface, lubri-

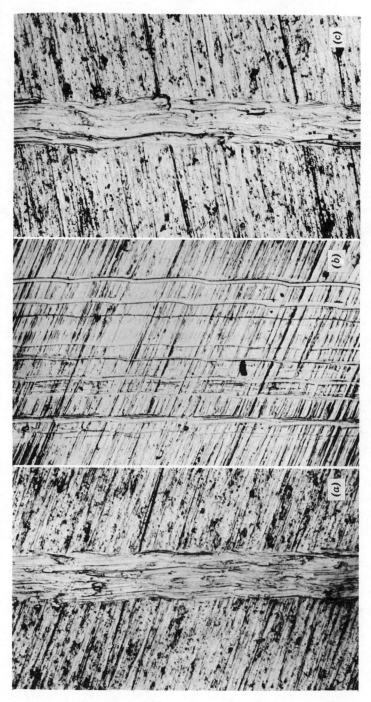

Fig. 6.20. Wear tracks for: (a) a titanium rider sliding on a titanium flat; (b) a titanium rider sliding on a 1020 steel flat; (c) a 1020 steel rider sliding on a titanium flat. Magnification ×130. Load 100 gm. No lubricant. Micrographs (a) and (c) look alike because the steel rider of (c) has been covered with titanium particles.

cated in the same way, gives a value of 0.09, as does steel sliding on steel.

Consequently, it is of importance in designing sliding systems of titanium against other materials that the titanium surface be made much smaller; for example, in a piston-cylinder combination, the titanium should be the piston, and its surface area should be reduced as much as possible.

6.13   Factors Which Lead to Complete Coverage of a Material by Fragments

In earlier sections we saw that complete coverage of one surface by fragments of the other material could be due to one of two causes.

1. The concentration of fragments as given by eq. 6.13 is high, larger than about 10% (Section 6.12).

2. The fragments initially transferred are tightly held and can pull off more fragments (Section 6.10).

The first of these factors is clearly due to a high value of r/p, where r is the probability of transfer of the material to the other surface and p is the probability of transfer of the material to itself. In general, high values of r/p are produced in systems in which there is a strong attraction between the sliding materials. Quantitatively, we may regard this strong attraction as arising from a high value of W_{ab}, the energy of adhesion (Machlin and Yankee, 1954). If W_{ab} is nearly as large as W_{aa}, the energy of cohesion of one of the surfaces, then a high degree of coverage of the surface of a by wear particles of b is likely. Without going into the situation quantitatively, it seems clear that if W_{ab} is comparable in magnitude with W_{aa}, the work of adhesion of material a to itself, then p and r are likely to be of the same order of magnitude; and, hence, $r/(p + r)$ may readily reach 50%. Materials similar in composition, for example, different alloys of the same metal such as the phosphor bronze and beryllium copper of Table 6.3, often show this effect, as do soft materials sliding against hard ones, for which system W_{ab} of the soft against the hard material may well exceed W_{aa} of the softer material. This accounts for the way that soft materials tend to smear onto and cover harder materials, for example, plastics on to metals, soft metals on to harder metals (Section 6.11).

As regards the second factor leading to complete coverage, that due to the tight adhesion of fragments to their substrate so that further fragments are transferred, we shall see later that this is accomplished if the ratio of surface energy to hardness, namely W_{ab}/p, is high.

Thus the two criteria are quite similar in that a high value of W_{ab} constitutes the prime condition for strong adhesion of the fragments.

6.14   Formation of Loose Wear Particles

Our discussion of the wear process has, so far, been oriented toward describing the formation of adherent wear fragments.   It is a matter of common observation however, that the sliding of two surfaces generally leads to loss of material from the system, and hence, loose particles must occur.   This formation of loose particles through the adhesive wear process involves an apparent contradiction, since the production of the initially adherent fragments presupposes a strong bond between the fragments and the surface on to which they are transferred, whereas the final loose particle formation, on the other hand, implies a weak bond.   The formation of loose particles is often a result of chemical changes in the adherent fragments.   Thus, if our sliding system contains steel, steel adherent fragments will be formed.   These fragments tend to oxidize, mainly to Fe_2O_3, which comes off loose.   Thereupon the surface to which the steel fragments were attached becomes available for the transfer of new steel particles.   It follows that, in this two-stage process, loose particles are formed from the adherent particles on the other sliding surface, and loose particles are not formed directly from the bulk sliding surface (Kerridge, 1955).

A second more general, mechanism which often operates so as to produce loose particles, involves the residual elastic energy of adherent fragments.   If we take a look at a fragment on the surface (Fig. 6.21), we see that, at the instant that it is formed in mating contact with the other surface, it is in a state of severe stress and strain; however, once the other surface has moved on, only residual stresses and strains remain.   These arise from the need of the fragment and its substrate to continue to conform geometrically at their mating surface.   For a particle to come off loose, the elastic energy stored in the particle while it is being formed must equal or exceed the energy of adhesion which binds it to its substrate.   Usually when a wear particle is made up by the aggregation of smaller fragments, the particle will come off loose as soon as its elastic energy becomes as large as its adhesive energy.

We assume a model in which an asperity with a flat end slides over another surface, adheres at one spot, and then shear occurs within the asperity so that a fragment is formed as shown in Fig. 6.22.   While the fragment was still attached to the asperity, it carried a high compressive stress, and consequently there were expansion strains in the other two, horizontal directions, each being of magnitude $v\sigma/E$, where

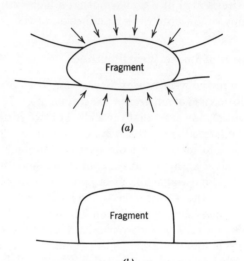

Fragment

(a)

Fragment

(b)

Fig. 6.21. Appearance of typical fragment (a) as formed under high stresses; (b) after other surface has moved on. Residual stresses remain to keep fragment and substrate in conformance.

ν is Poisson's ratio, σ the normal compressive stress, and E the Young's modulus. After the fragment is formed, the normal stress is gone, but the horizontal strains will remain, because adhesion at the interface will tend to prevent the fragment from contracting. Thus, residual stresses will be set up, of magnitude $\nu\sigma$. If we assume that the initial normal stress was the yield stress σ_y for the material, which is the maximum the material can carry without plastic yielding, the residual stresses will be $\nu\sigma_y$.

It will be appreciated that this discussion has been based on an over-simplified model of the events, occurring at the asperity, which give rise to the formation of a fragment. It is believed, however, that our expression for the residual stress is not far from the true value.

If we assume that the wear particle has a shape which approximates that of a hemisphere, we may write the elastic energy E_e stored in it, in the form

$$E_e = \left(\frac{\nu^2\sigma_y^{\,2}}{2E}\right)\left(\frac{\pi d^3}{12}\right) \tag{6.20}$$

The adhesional energy E_a acting over the interface may be written as

$$E_a = W_{ab}\left(\frac{\pi d^2}{4}\right) \qquad (6.21)$$

where W_{ab} is the work of adhesion of the contacting materials.

A particle can come off if $E_e \geqslant E_a$, since then the removal of the particle will minimize the free energy of the system as a whole.

By applying this condition, we obtain

$$d \geqslant \frac{6EW_{ab}}{\nu^2 \sigma_y^2} \qquad (6.22)$$

In the great majority of cases, especially for systems in which the normal load is small, it is found that the wear particles initially transferred are too small to satisfy the equation. Instead, the transferred

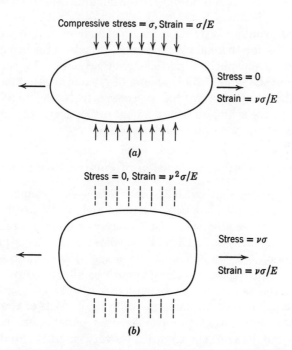

Fig. 6.22. Hypothetical and greatly simplified stress and strain picture of a fragment. (a) At the instant of formation; (b) after normal stress has been removed.

wear particles grow by accretion of further wear debris (Cocks, 1964) until a large enough wear particle is formed. For a system of this kind, eq. 6.22 becomes a straight equality.

We may simplify eq. 6.22 by noting that ν^2 is about $\frac{1}{10}$ for most materials, and that σ_y is about $\frac{1}{3}$ the penetration hardness p, which can be more readily measured than can the yield strength. Furthermore, the ratio σ_y/E is fairly constant for most materials, its average value being about 3×10^{-3}. Thus, our condition for loose particle formation becomes

$$d = 60,000\,\frac{W_{ab}}{p} \qquad (6.23)$$

This is a relation between a measurable quantity (the diameter of loose wear particles) and the two material properties p and W_{ab} which involves no unknown quantities, and may thus be checked experimentally.

Equation 6.23 is unusual in that the nondimensional constant which appears in it is surprisingly large. The $\frac{1}{60,000}$ with which d must be multiplied to obtain W_{ab}/p is made up of a factor of $\frac{1}{10}$ representing ν^2, a factor of $\frac{1}{2}$ for the energy expression, a factor of $\frac{1}{3}$ being the shape factor for a hemispherical particle, another factor of $\frac{1}{3}$ corresponding to the σ_y/p ratio; and, finally, a factor of $\frac{1}{333}$ representing the maximum elastic strain. Owing to the successive multiplications, the small W_{ab}/p distance is amplified into a quantity, namely, the wear particle diameter, which takes on considerable size.

6.15   Experimental Verification of Particle Size Equation

It will be seen that eq. 6.23 postulates a very simple relationship between the size of *loose* wear particles and the W_{ab}/p ratio. Since the wear particles produced by a sliding system cover a range of sizes, it is clear that d in eq. 6.23 must be some average wear particle size. As in Section 6.5, we define the "average" fragment so that all the fragments larger than it weigh as much as all the fragments smaller than it, and d as its average dimension.

Experimental verification of eq. 6.23 then consists of two steps, first the demonstration that the average wear particle size is a *material* property and does not change when we vary external variables such as load, speed, and duration of sliding, while keeping W_{ab} and p constant. Second, that the particle size does change when we vary W_{ab} and p, and that the constant of proportionality in eq. 6.23 is 60,000.

As regards the first step, we show in the Figs. 6.23 to 6.25, and

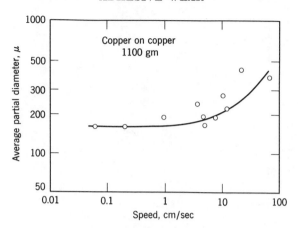

Fig. 6.23.   Plot of average wear particle diameter as a function of surface speed.

Table 6.4, data on the effect of speed, load, crystal grain size, and duration of sliding.   Figure 6.23 shows data on the particle size produced by copper on copper annular cylinder specimens as a function of sliding speed.   For speeds of 0.1 to 10 cm/sec the particle size is almost independent of speed, thereafter there is a small degree of dependence, which is exaggerated on the graph because the vertical scale has been greatly expanded compared to the horizontal.   The particle size variation appears to be associated with the onset of severe vibration of the sliding system, which in turn produces shock loading. This effect is considered next.

Figure 6.24 shows data obtained on the effect of load on wear particle size.   At loads below 100 gm, the dependence of wear particle size on load is small, but at higher loads there is some dependence.   This increase of particle size with increased load is associated with the fact that, in eq. 6.23, it was assumed that loose wear particles were built up by the agglomeration of smaller transferred particles.   At heavy loads a substantial fraction of the transferred particles are apparently formed initially with dimensions exceeding the minimum required for loose particle formation, and they come off loose immediately.

Figure 6.25 shows some data on the effect of grain size of copper specimens on particle size.   It has often been thought that there might be a connection between wear particle size and the grain size of the metal wearing away.   Tests carried out with copper of widely differing grain size suggest that this effect is very small.   Certainly there is no proportionality, or nothing resembling a proportionality, between the wear particle size and the grain size, as Fig. 6.25 bears out.

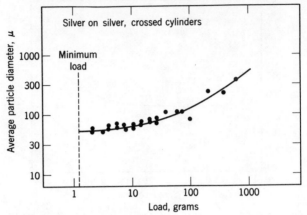

Fig. 6.24. Plot of average particle diameter against load for silver or silver sliding specimens.

The effect of distance of sliding on the wear particle size is shown in Table 6.4. These data were obtained with annular copper specimens, and for this system the amount of wear decreases markedly with distance of sliding, because the annuli eventually interlock each other quite effectively and make it difficult for wear particles to escape. However, the loose particle diameter remains almost constant.

Having shown that d is almost unaffected by external parameters such as load, speed, grain size, and distance of sliding, we are now in a

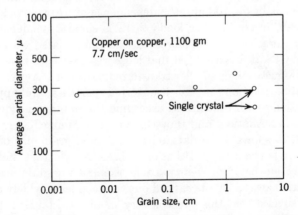

Fig. 6.25. Plot of average wear particle diameter against metal grain size (varied as a result of heat treatment) for copper specimens.

Table 6.4. Wear of Copper Surfaces as a Function of Distance of Sliding

Number of Revolutions	Total Wear	Wear per Revolution	Average Fragment Diameter
10	0.0015 gm	0.15 mg/rev	
40	0.0125	0.31	
160	0.0271	0.17	240 μ
640	0.0567	0.089	225 μ
2880	0.1242	0.043	260 μ
11520	0.2756	0.024	290 μ

position to determine whether d does vary in accordance with eq. 6.23 when the surface energy and the hardness are varied. The best way of varying the surface energy while keeping the hardness constant is to consider one material and to change the environment so as to vary the surface characteristics. Data obtained in this way with copper surfaces are shown in Table 6.5.

It will be seen that inert atmospheres such as nitrogen and helium, which would be expected to leave very clean copper surfaces, give the largest wear particles, whereas reactive atmospheres lead to the production of much smaller particles. In the presence of liquid lubricants a further drastic drop in particle size occurs, and again the most

Table 6.5. Size of Copper Wear Particles in Various Environments

Environment	Average Fragment Diameter
Nitrogen	480μ
Helium	380
Carbon dioxide	300
Dry air	224
Oxygen	201
Laboratory air	177
Wet air	144
Cetane	12.0
Silicone DC 200–100 cst.	9.5
Ucon fluid LB-70X	9.5
Palmitic acid in cetane	8.0

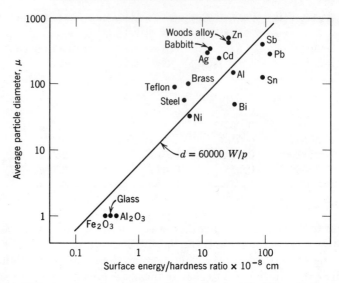

Fig. 6.26.   Plot of average wear particle diameter against the W/p ratio for metallic and nonmetallic materials.

reactive lubricants produce the smallest wear particles.   These results are certainly qualitatively consistant with eq. 6.23.

A more rigorous quantitative test of eq. 6.23 is obtained when sliding tests are carried out on a variety of materials, metals and nonmetals, and the measured wear particle size is plotted against the computed W/p ratio.   Figure 6.26 shows the result of such an experiment.   It will be seen that d does indeed vary more or less proportionately with W/p, and that the constant of proportionality does indeed have the very large and unusual value of 60,000.

These results, taken all in all, may be considered to be quite satisfactory confirmation of eq. 6.23.   The fact that the formation of loose wear particles does appear to be governed by such simple factors encourages us to try and apply the same kind of argument to analogous situations.   The one that appears to be most promising is that involving the minimum load for wear particle formation.

6.16   Minimum Load for Loose Particle Formation

According to the plastic deformation theory of friction, we have (eq. 3.2)

$$L = Ap$$

where L is the total normal load and A the real area of contact. In the limiting case of all the load carried by one circular junction d, we have

$$L = \frac{\pi d^2 p}{4} \qquad (6.24)$$

Now if the load is small, the diameter of the junction will be small, and the region near the junction which is given elastic energy of deformation is small, and any particle which could be formed from the junction is small. But there is a minimum size of a loose wear particle, and hence a minimum size of a junction from which the particle is formed, with a corresponding minimum load.

The average wear particle size is given by eq. 6.23, but it is found in practice that the particles have a spread in size by almost a factor of 3 about the average, so that we may write the minimum particle diameter $d_{\min}$ in the form

$$d_{\min} = 20,000 \, \frac{W_{ab}}{p} \qquad (6.25)$$

If now we equate d from eq. 6.24 with the $d_{\min}$ of eq. 6.25, we may combine these two equations and obtain

$$L_{\min} = \pi \times 10^8 \, \frac{W_{ab}^2}{p} \qquad (6.26)$$

This represents the load which would produce a circular area or contact whose diameter is the same as that of the minimum weaf particle.

Perhaps we can make this discussion a little more concrete by considering an actual material, namely a noble metal such as silver, gold, or platinum. For the pure metal in the work-hardened state, we have p about 120 kg/mm^2, or 1.2×10^{10} dynes/cm^2, and W_{ab} about 1000 erg/cm^2.

Then
$$d_{av} \, (= 60,000 \, W_{ab}/p) = 5 \times 10^{-3} \text{ cm}$$

$$d_{\min} \, (= 20,000 \, W_{ab}/p) = 1.7 \times 10^{-3} \text{ cm}$$

$$L_{\min} \, (= \pi \times 10^8 \, W_{ab}^2/p) = 25 \text{ gm}$$

Here then is another result derived through the use of the surface energy concept which we can test experimentally. First, when noble metals are slid together we predict a minimum load, below which no loose wear particles will form (and hence no overall loss of weight will occur), although there may well be fragments transferred to and from

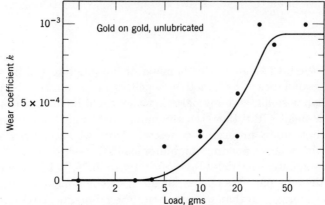

Fig. 6.27.   Loss in weight of a gold on gold sliding system as a function of load.

between the surfaces.   Second, this minimum load will be about 25 gm.

Experimental tests show that for gold on gold, there is indeed a minimum load (Fig. 6.27) below which no overall loss of weight from the sliding specimens occurs, and no wear particles form, even after prolonged sliding (up to 2 weeks).   It is found that the actual minimum load is 5 gm, rather than the predicted 25 gm.

It is not quite clear how this difference arises, but it probably relates to the fact that noble metals tend to build up clumps of particles (or prows) in front of the rider (Fig. 6.28), these particles being considerably larger than the real area of contact (Cocks, 1962; Antler, 1963).

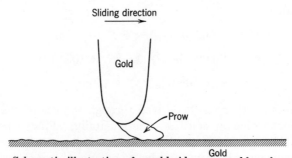

Fig. 6.28.   Schematic illustration of a gold rider on a gold surface, showing the formation of a prow or very large particle.

6.17 The Size of Transferred Particles and the Minimum Load for Transfer

Because the prows upset our model of the wear process (they have a much greater ratio of elastic energy to energy of adhesion than do hemispherical particles), we must proceed to calculate the conditions under which prows are formed. Since prows are made up of transferred adhering particles, we must set up the condition for the transfer of a particle (which process is necessary but not sufficient for the formation of prows). Figure 6.29 shows a possible model of the adhesive wear process, in which a junction has been formed between materials a and b, and a hemispherical particle is about to be formed as shown. We assume that the condition for particle formation is that the total elastic energy contained in the hemisphere is at least equal to the surface energy of the hemisphere. That is to say:

$$\frac{1}{2} \cdot \frac{\sigma_y^{\,2}}{E} \cdot \frac{\pi d^3}{12} = \frac{\pi d^2}{2} \cdot 2\gamma_a$$

or
$$d = \frac{24\gamma_a E}{\sigma_y^{\,2}} \tag{6.27}$$

As before (eq. 6.22) and 6.23) we set $\sigma_y/E = 3.10^{-3}$, $\sigma_y = p/3$. This gives

$$d = \frac{24000\gamma_a}{p} \tag{6.28}$$

(Note: this derivation for the size of adherent particles is not too satisfactory, since it ignores the interface between materials a and b. It is easy to show, however, that eq. 6.28 is essentially correct for any process in which elastic volume energy is converted to surface energy of particles. For the simplest case of a body of volume 1 cm^3, given

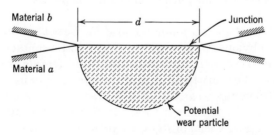

Fig. 6.29. Model of a junction at which a transferred particle is about to be formed.

its maximum elastic energy and then broken up into cubes of diameter d, we have

$$\frac{1}{2} \cdot \frac{\sigma_y^2}{E} = \frac{6\gamma_a d^2}{d^3} \tag{6.29}$$

$$\therefore d = \frac{12\gamma_a E}{\sigma_y^2} = \frac{12000\gamma_a}{p} \tag{6.30}$$

which differs from eq. 6.28 by only a factor of two.)

From eq. 6.28, the diameter of the average adherent particle is, for like materials such as gold on gold, exactly one-fifth as great as the diameter of loose fragments, since for like metals W_{ab} is just twice γ_a.

For the gold on gold system, we therefore have

Diameter of average adherent particle $= 10^{-3}$ cm
Diameter of least adherent particle $= 3 \cdot 3 \times 10^{-4}$ cm (presumably)
Load corresponding to least adherent particle $= 1$ gm

Since according to the foregoing relation no adherent particles can form at loads below 1 gm, it is clear that no prows, which constitute an agglomeration of such particles, can form either, and hence no loose particles can be produced. As we have seen in Fig. 6.27, in practice loose wear particles cease to be formed at loads below 5 gm, and it is found that the formation of prows ceases at about the same load.

When sliding experiments are carried out at loads below the limit of formation of transferred fragments, a new phenomenon is observed. It is found that the surfaces take on a smooth appearance, rather akin to that observed during polishing (Fig. 6.30). Apparently, the energy associated with sliding is sufficient to plastically deform the surface asperities (by shear) and hence change the surface appearance, as long as no increase of free surface area (corresponding to the formation of particles) occurs. Instead, deformation occurs in such a way that the surface energy (and hence the surface area) is minimized. For the relationship between this phenomenon and the process of polishing see Section 7.8.

The fact that there is a minimum load for wear to occur appears to find its most obvious application in sliding electric contacts that carry very small electric currents (i.e., those that transfer information rather than energy). For this application it is customary to use noble metal alloys, and then the wear rate can be reduced very drastically by reducing the load per contact to about 1 gm. Thus 10 contacts in parallel, each under a load of 1 gm, are preferable to one contact under a load of 10 gm.

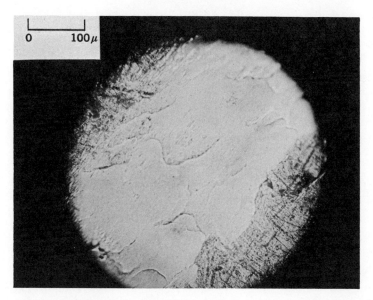

Fig. 6.30. Silver surface after sliding test at a load of 0.2 gm. The center of the friction track has taken on a polished appearance.

The minimum load concept cannot as readily be applied to the common oxide-forming metals such as copper or steel. It is found that sliding systems of these metals can produce either large metal particles, with dimensions given by eq. 6.23 when W_{ab} and p of the metal are used, or small oxide particles, with dimensions again given by eq. 6.23, but this time for values of W_{ab} and p characteristic of the oxide. Thus, low carbon steel systems give both steel particles of diameter 60μ, and oxide particles of diameter $1~\mu$. At low humidity and high load the particles that come off in loose form are predominantly metallic, whereas at low load and high humidity they are mainly oxide.

The existence of two possible solutions to eq. 6.23 means that we must consider a minimum load so small that neither oxide nor metal particles can form. Since oxide particles are only about $1~\mu$ in diameter, the minimum load works out to be in the milligram range, a value so low that it has little practical interest.

6.18   Materials To Be Used in Adhesive Wear Situations

In those situations—the great majority—where our main interest lies in reducing the amount of wear, we select our materials in accord-

Table 6.6.   Typical Values of Coefficient of Wear k

Condition	Metal (on Metal)		Non-Metal (on Metal)
	Like	Unlike	
Clean	$5 \cdot 10^{-3}$	$2 \cdot 10^{-4}$	$5 \cdot 10^{-6}$
Poorly lubricated	$2 \cdot 10^{-4}$	$2 \cdot 10^{-4}$	$5 \cdot 10^{-6}$
Average lubrication	$2 \cdot 10^{-5}$	$2 \cdot 10^{-5}$	$5 \cdot 10^{-6}$
Excellent lubrication	$2 \cdot 10^{-6}$–10^{-7}	$2 \cdot 10^{-6}$–10^{-7}	$2 \cdot 10^{-6}$

ance with eq. 6.7, and the general outline of the values of k as given in Table 6.6.

These data suggest the following rules:

1. Use *hard* materials
2. Use materials with *low interaction*, either combinations which will give a low intrinsic value of W_{ab} (at least one member of the pair a non-metal, or two metals with very low interaction, Section 4.7) or else use combinations with a high value of W_{ab} (two metals), and reduce W_{ab} by the use of a good boundary lubricant.

As regards the use of hard materials, it should be pointed out that this does not generally produce very drastic effects. Thus, assume that we have an alloy steel which when half-hard has a Rockwell C value of 40 ($\sim$400 kg/mm^2), and when fully hard has a Rockwell C hardness of 60 ($\sim$800 kg/mm^2). This difference by a factor of two in hardness will produce a difference by a factor of two in the adhesive wear rate, which is only just large enough to be measurable, since the difference between repeat wear tests under identical conditions is likely to be a factor of three!

But we must not overlook the fact that the difference in hardness is likely to bring with it marked difference in chemical structure, perhaps a change from a predominantly iron structure to a predominantly iron carbide composition. Iron carbide, not being a metal but a metalloid material, is likely to have a lower surface energy than iron, and thus a lower interaction with other materials. This means that it will have a much lower value of k than does iron when it is unlubricated, but a slightly higher value of k than does iron when covered by a good boundary lubricant. These chemical changes are likely to produce factor-of-10 changes in the wear rate, making them more important than the factor-of-2 changes produced by the hardness variation itself.

The reader may wonder at this point why, in many applications, great care is taken to harden steel sliding surfaces almost to the limit. The reason is that the main solid contaminant likely to be introduced into sliding systems is silica (sand), and this has a hardness of about 800 kg/mm^2. Thus the change from a hardness level of 400 to one of 900 kg/mm^2 eliminates abrasive wear which might result from the silica.

Some time ago it was considered axiomatic that a sliding system should consist of one soft and one hard surface. This is excellent practice for lubricated bearings, where a hard steel shaft and a soft bearing metal are used to great advantage. But this system operates well only if a good lubricant is available, otherwise wear of the soft metal would become excessive. The use of a soft bearing material is of advantage only where abrasive particles might be carried by the lubricant, which could be trapped in the soft metal (see Section 7.7), or if the readier deformation of the soft metal can help in aligning the bearing surfaces so that hydrodynamic bearing action is achieved.

In situations where these factors are not of importance, it may be preferable to use two hard surfaces. The classification of materials in the order

Diamond

Boron carbide

(Silicon carbide, aluminum oxide)

Tungsten and/or titanium carbide

Nitrided steel

Carburized steel

gives a list in order of decreasing wear resistance but increasing desirability as regards cost of materials and their processing. Although any of these materials can probably be safely used sliding against itself, it is frequent practice to resort to unlike combinations, for example a nitrided steel on a carburized steel. This certainly does no harm.

For moderate cost applications in which relatively large amounts of wear can be tolerated, one of the sliding surfaces is often made of a low carbon or a medium carbon steel alloy. The other surface is then generally a material compatible with steel, namely, a brass or a bronze alloy, or cast iron, or an aluminum bronze (Kolesnikova and Beloiusov, 1960; Angus 1957). Plastic bearings are frequently used (Pinchbeck, 1962).

Sintered metal powder compacts are frequently used as bearing materials; not only do the pores act as reservoirs for lubricant, but the fact that each junction is small tends to prevent adhesive wear.

References

Angus, H. T. (1957), The Wear of Cast Iron Machine Tool Slides, Shears and Guideways, *Wear*, **1**, 40–57.

Antler, M. (1963), The Lubrication of Gold, *Wear*, **6**, 44–65.

Archard, J. F. (1953), Contact and Rubbing of Flat Surfaces, *J. Appl. Phys.*, **24**, 981–988.

Bikerman, J. J. (1962), Science of Adhesive Joints, published in *Adhesion and Cohesion*, P. Weiss, ed., Elsevier, Amsterdam, pp. 36–43.

Bowden, F. P., L. Leben, and D. Tabor (1939), The Sliding of Metals, Frictional Fluctuations and Vibration of Moving Parts, *Engineer (London)*, **168**, 214–220.

Burwell, J. T., and C. D. Strang (1952), On the Empirical Law of Adhesive Wear, *J. Appl. Phys.*, **23**, 18–28.

Cocks, M. (1962), Interaction of Sliding Metal Surfaces, *J. Appl. Phys.*, **33**, 2152–2161.

Cocks, M. (1964), Role of Displaced Metal in the Sliding of Flat Metal Surfaces, *J. Appl. Phys.*, **35**, 1807–1814.

Einstein, A. (1905), On the Motion of Suspended Particles Produced by the Kinetic Theory of Heat, (in German), *Ann. Phys.*, **17**, 549–560.

Feng, I-M. (1952), Metal Transfer and Wear, *J. Appl. Phys.*, **23**, 1011–1019.

Green, A. P. (1955), Friction between Unlubricated Metals: A Theoretical Analysis of the Junction Model, *Proc. Roy. Soc.*, A **228**, 181–204.

Greenwood, J. A., and D. Tabor (1955), Deformation Properties of Friction Junctions, *Proc. Phys. Soc. (London)*, **68 B**, 609–619.

Greenwood, J. A., and D. Tabor (1957), The Properties of Model Friction Junctions, Published in *Conference on Lubrication and Wear*, Institution Mech. Eng., London, 314–317.

Holm, R. (1946), *Electric Contacts*, Almqvist and Wiksells, Stockholm.

Kerridge, M. (1955), Metal Transfer and the Wear Process, *Proc. Phys. Soc. (London)* **68 B**, 400–407.

Kolesnikova, V. S., and N. N. Beloiusov (1960), Investigation of the Anti-Friction Properties of Some Bronzes and Brasses, published in *Friction and Wear in Machinery*, translated by the A.S.M.E., New York, **14**, 87–153.

Machlin, E. S., and W. R. Yankee (1954), Friction of Clean Metals and Oxides with Special Reference to Titanium, *J. Appl. Phys.*, **25**, 576–581.

Pinchbeck, P. H. (1962), A Review of Plastic Bearings, *Wear*, **5**, 85–113.

Rabinowicz, E. (1951), The Nature of the Static and Kinetic Coefficients of Friction, *J. Appl. Phys.*, **22**, 1373–1379.

Rabinowicz, E. (1953), A Quantitative Study of the Wear Process, *Proc. Phys. Soc. (London)* **66 B**, 929–936.

Rabinowicz, E., and D. Tabor (1951), Metallic Transfer between Sliding Metals: An Autoradiographic Study, *Proc. Roy. Soc.*, A **208**, 455–475.

Rabinowicz, E., and K. V. Shooter (1952), The Transfer of Metal to Plastics during Sliding, *Proc. Phys. Soc.*, **65 B**, 671–673.

Sakmann, B. W., J. T. Burwell, and J. W. Irvine (1944), Measurement of the Adhesion Component of Friction by Means of Radioactive Indicators, *J. Appl. Phys.* **15**, 459–473.

7

Abrasive and Other
Types of Wear

7.1 Introduction

This form of wear arises when a hard, rough surface slides against a softer surface, digs into it, and plows a series of grooves. The material originally in the grooves is normally removed in the form of loose fragments.

Abrasive wear can also arise in a somewhat different situation, when hard, abrasive particles are introduced between sliding surfaces and abrade material off each. The mechanism of this form of abrasive wear seems to be that an abrasive grain adheres temporarily to one of the sliding surfaces, or else is embedded in it, and plows out a groove in the other. The two forms of wear, one involving a hard, rough surface and the other hard, abrasive grains, are generally referred to as the two-body and the three-body abrasive wear process respectively (Burwell, 1957).

Abrasive wear of the two-body kind does not take place when the hard, sliding surface is smooth. Similarly, three-body abrasive wear does not occur when the particles in the system are small, or when they are softer than the sliding materials. Hence it is usually possible to arrange matters so that a sliding system is, initially at any rate, free from abrasive wear. Once sliding has commenced, however, abrasive wear may become a problem, as wear debris, often made harder by oxidation, begins to accumulate in the system as result of other wear processes. In other cases contaminating particles may be introduced into the sliding system from the environment.

Abrasive wear is very widely used in material finishing operations.

The two-body type of abrasive wear is made use of in files, abrasive paper, abrasive cloth, and abrasive wheels, whereas the three-body type of wear is used for lapping and polishing.   As we shall see later, it is the simplicity and reproducibility of the abrasive wear process that makes the use of abrasive wear so attractive.

7.2   Quantitative Expression for Abrasive Wear

To derive a quantitative expression for abrasive wear, we may consider a simple model in which the asperities on the hard surface are conical (Fig. 7.1).   Confining ourselves initially to one asperity carrying a load ΔL, we find (eq. 3.2) that it will penetrate the softer surface to an extent given by

$$\Delta L = p \cdot \Delta A = p \cdot \pi r^2$$

where p is the hardness of the softer surface.

The projected area of the penetrating cone in the vertical plane is rx. Thus when the cone moves through a distance dl, it will sweep out a volume dV given by

$$dV = r \cdot x \cdot dl = r^2 \cdot \tan \theta \cdot dl = \frac{\Delta L \cdot \tan \theta \cdot dl}{\pi p} \tag{7.1}$$

$$\frac{dV}{dl} = \frac{\Delta L \cdot \tan \theta}{\pi p}$$

If we now add the contributions of all the asperities, we will have

$$\frac{dV}{dl} = \frac{L \, \overline{\tan \theta}}{\pi p} \tag{7.2}$$

where $\overline{\tan \theta}$ is a weighted average of the $\tan \theta$ values of all the individual cones.

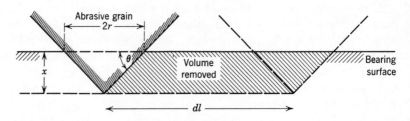

Fig. 7.1. Abrasive wear model in which a cone removes material from a surface. This model represents a considera1 oversimplification.

Table 7.1.   Abrasive Wear Constants k

Investigator	Wear Type	Size (μ)	Materials	$k(\times 10^{-3})$
Spurr et al. (1957)	2-body	—	Many	180
Spurr et al. (1957)	2-body	110	Many	150
Avient et al. (1960)	2-body	40–150	Many	120
Lopa (1956)	2-body	260	Steel	80
Kruschov et al. (1958)	2-body	80	Many	24
Samuels (1956)	2-body	70	Brass	16
Toporov (1958)	3-body	150	Steel	6
Rabinowicz et al. (1961a)	3-body	80	Steel	4.5
Rabinowicz et al. (1961b)	3-body	40	Many	2

This equation has, quite fortuitously, the same form as eq. 6.6, with the term $\overline{\tan \theta}/\pi$ replacing $k/3$. Accordingly, we shall analyze abrasive wear in terms of eq. 6.6, calculating values of k_{abr}, which will be related to the roughness values of the hypothetical cones, according to the equation

$$k_{\mathrm{abr}} = 0.96 \, \overline{\tan \theta} \qquad (7.3)$$

Typical values of k_{abr} are given in Table 7.1. It will be seen that coefficients of wear in the two-body case are in the range 2.10^{-1} to 2.10^{-2}, whereas in the three-body case they are about an order of magnitude smaller—namely, 10^{-2} to 10^{-3}. Since there is nothing to suggest that the abrading geometry is different in the two cases, it seems that the abrasive grains in the three-body case spend about 90% of the time rolling, thus producing no abrasive wear particles, and only about 10% of the time sliding and abrading the surfaces. This would explain the low coefficient of friction which we have measured during three-body abrasion—namely, $f = 0.25$, as against $f = 0.60$ for two-body abrasion.

Mulhearn and Samuels (1962) have shown that eq. 7.2 is a severe oversimplification, in that, for a typical silicon carbide paper, $\tan \theta$ has a value of about $\frac{1}{3}$, but only about $\frac{1}{8}$th of the emery grains are in cutting position (the others carry load, but do not cut). Accordingly, the overall value of k in this case drops to $(\frac{1}{3}) \times (\frac{1}{8})$, or about 4%.

7.3   Experimental Evidence for the Abrasive Wear Equation

Although there have been a number of formulations of the abrasive wear process which are far more complete and complex than eq. 7.2, for

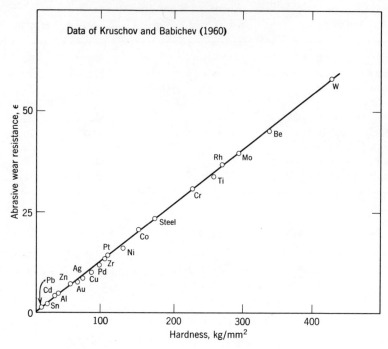

Fig. 7.2.   Wear resistance of pure metals, two-body abrasion.

example Mulhearn and Samuels (1962), Goddard and Wilman (1962), it nevertheless appears to be a well established fact that the observed wear rate is indeed proportional to the load, proportional to the distance of sliding, and inversely proportional to the hardness.

The effect of hardness is shown most clearly in the work of Kruschov (1957), who has shown that the inverse of the abrasive wear rate dV/dl, namely dl/dV (which he calls the wear resistance ϵ) is proportional to the hardness for a large number of pure metals (Fig. 7.2). Similar results have been obtained by Rabinowicz, Dunn, and Russell (1961b) under three-body conditions (Fig. 7.3).

The dependence of abrasive wear on distance of sliding is rather more complex.   In situations where abrasion always takes place with fresh abrasive paper or fresh abrasive particles, the wear continues at a steady rate, although there is sometimes an initial period when the wear rate is abnormally low (Fig. 7.4).   During this initial period some abrasive particles adhere to the wearing surface.   A very similar curve, showing initial low wear, and later a uniform rate of wear, for a system

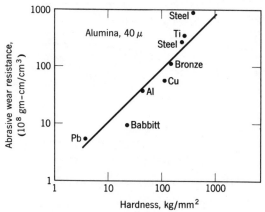

Fig. 7.3.   Wear resistance of metals during three-body abrasion.

in which rock salt is abraded by silicon carbide under three-body conditions, is shown by Aleinikov (1957a).

But when the sliding system contains a limited amount of abrasive, which is used over and over again as sliding continues, the wear rate tends to drop off as sliding continues.   Mulhearn and Samuels (1962) have studied the wear rate as a function of time when steel is abraded on silicon carbide abrasive paper, and have found that their data fits an equation of the form

$$V = V_\infty (1 - e^{-\beta l}) \tag{7.4}$$

where V_∞ is the total volume of metal removed abrasively if the sliding

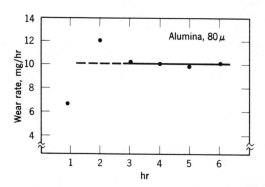

Fig. 7.4.   Abrasive wear rate of 52100 steel as function of time.   Load 1 kg, sliding speed 6 cm/sec.

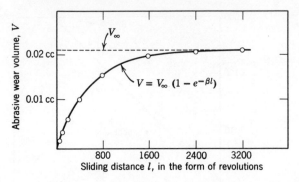

Fig. 7.5. Data of Mulhearn and Samuels (1962). Steel on 220 grade silicon carbide paper.

is continued indefinitely, and β is a constant. Their experimental data, as well as their equation, fitted with two constants V_∞ and β, is also shown (Fig. 7.5). According to eq. 7.4, the wear rate (dV/dl) is initially at a constant rate, but then gradually drops to zero.

Mulhearn and Samuels explain this eventual dropping off of the wear rate as due to blunting of the abrasive particles (Fig. 7.6). Another factor which is probably also present is the clogging of the paper by abraded particles derived from the material being abraded. This wear debris will eventually lift the material above the level of the abrasive grains in the paper, at which point abrasive action will cease (Fig. 7.7).

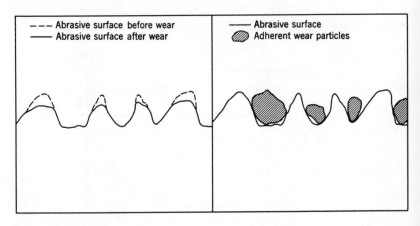

Fig. 7.6. Hypothetical appearance of abrasive surface before and after wear, showing blunting.

Fig. 7.7. Hypothetical abrasive surface clogged by wear debris.

In conformity with this explanation, it should be noted that according to Mulhearn and Samuels, abrasive action ceases much more rapidly with the fine than with the coarse grades of abrasive paper.

The variation of abrasive wear with load has been relatively little studied. According to Avient, Goddard, and Wilman (1960) who measured the mass loss during two-body abrasion while varying the applied load from 0.2 to 2 kg, the abrasive wear rate is indeed proportional to the load, as demanded by eq. 7.2.

The preceding discussion has given the impression that abrasive wear is a simple phenomenon which obeys simple rules. To a large extent this is true. There are a few complications which may arise, however, and these will be detailed next.

7.4 Effect of Hardness on Abrasive Wear Rate

As we have seen earlier, the abrasive wear rate of a surface, using any particular abrading medium, is inversely proportional to the hardness of the surface. Hence, a plot of the wear rate-hardness product against the hardness should be a horizontal line. Figure 7.8 gives data of Aleinikov (1957b); and it will be seen that, in practice, the plot is a horizontal line up to a certain point and then drops off markedly. (*Note:* Aleinikov feels that in the low hardness region his data, obtained on various brittle materials, obey a law of the type: "wear rate × hardness^2 = constant," but his data appear to be just as consistent with the "wear rate × hardness = constant" relationship of eq. 7.2.) A plot of the ratio of wear produced by an abrasive of medium hard-

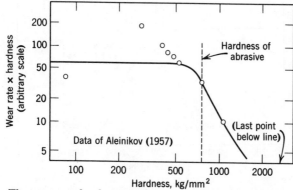

Fig. 7.8. The wear rate-hardness product drops off drastically when the material being abraded is harder than the abrasive.

ness, to that produced by a very hard abrasive, shows very clearly the effect of exceeding the hardness of the abrasive (Fig. 7.9).

The hardness value at which the abrasive wear rate drops off is very nearly equal to the hardness of the abrasive medium (Kruschov and Babichev, 1956). A little thought will show that this is an effect we might reasonably have expected. The fact that no abrasive will cut anything harder than itself is an important feature of the abrasive wear process that should always be kept in mind. When abrasive wear is required, the abrasive material must be harder than the surface to be abraded, but need not be enormously harder. When abrasive wear is unwanted, it can always be cured by making the sliding surfaces harder than the abrasive. In this context it is helpful to remember that the most common abrasive contaminant is sand (SiO_2) with a hardness of about 800 kg/mm^2. The most common engineering material is steel, whose hardness can be varied from 200 to 1000 kg/mm^2. Thus a very hard steel is not abraded by sand, but softer grades of steel are readily worn away.

The hardness limitation to the abrasive wear process, as discussed previously, forms the basis for the well-known Mohs's hardness scale, widely used by mineralogists. If mineral A is harder than mineral B, A scratches (i.e., abrades) B, but is not scratched in return. Thus a monotonic hardness scale can be set up. A comparison of Mohs's and Vickers hardness scales, taken from Tabor (1954), is shown in Fig. 7.10.

The other effect of hardness which must be considered is that arising

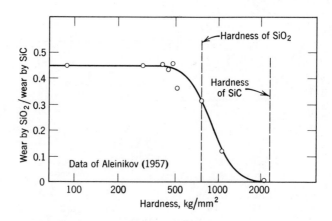

Fig. 7.9.   Comparison of wear produced by SiO_2 and SiC abrasives.   The ratio drops to zero when surfaces much harder than SiO_2 are abraded.

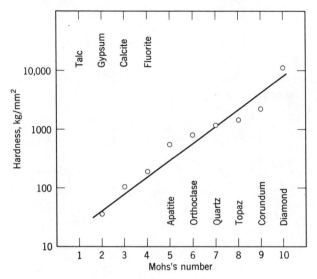

Fig. 7.10.   Plot (derived from Tabor, 1954) of hardness as a function of Mohs's number.

in cases in which the abrasive and the material being abraded remain fixed, but the heat treatment of the abraded material is varied, thus producing a change of hardness.   It has been shown by Kruschov (1957) that when steel alloys are used, the increase of hardness brings with it an increase of wear resistance, but not as great as is indicated in eq. 7.2 or shown in Figs. 7.2 and 7.3.   Some of our data on the wear resistance of bearing steels, which show the effects described by Kruschov very clearly, are plotted in Fig. 7.11.   It will be seen that the points for the steel in a soft condition do lie on the dashed line, but that the harder modifications of the steels fall well below the line.   On the whole, the wear resistance of the steel varies as approximately the $\frac{1}{3}$ power of the hardness (Rabinowicz, Dunn, and Russell, 1951a).

It should be stated at the outset that it is very difficult to explain this last effect.   Probably there is no single cause for the anomalous behavior, but we must consider a number of factors, all of which may play a part.   First, there is the factor of brittleness.   If a material is hardened, it generally becomes more brittle; and, hence, there is the possibility that, during abrasion, a wear particle is produced which is greater than the geometrical size of the wear groove.   Indeed, we have observed very high wear rates with very hard, brittle, steel specimens.

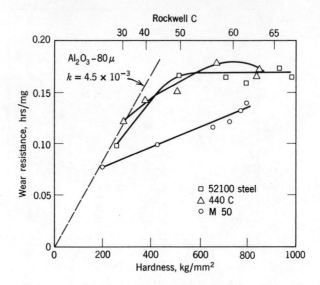

Fig. 7.11.   Wear resistance as a function of hardness for three bearing steels heat treated in various ways.

Then there is the matter of the indentation shape.   Tabor (1951) shows that for annealed metals the material displaced by a hardness indentation forms a raised hill above the original surface at a great distance from the indentation, whereas with hardened metals the raised hill is formed very close to the indentation (Fig. 7.12).   In abrasive wear testing this effect increases the volume which is abraded away in hardened materials, as against that removed in annealed materials. These factors, and perhaps other, combine to produce the fractional increase of wear resistance with hardness of hardened metals.

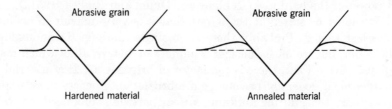

Fig. 7.12.   Schematic illustration of the indentation of an abrasive grain into a hardened and an annealed material.

7.5 Influence of Abrasive Particle Size on Abrasive Wear Rate

Many investigators (Avient, Goddard, and Wilman, 1960; Rabinowicz, Dunn, and Russell, 1961b; Kruschov and Babichev, 1960; Mulhearn and Samuels, 1962), have found that when the materials and the abrasive remain fixed, but the size of the abrasive is varied, there is a critical abrasive particle size such that the wear rate is independent of abrasive particle size when the latter is above the critical value, but there is a strong dependence of wear rate on particle size below the critical size.   Typical data are shown in Fig. 7.13.

In explaining this behavior we note that, in eq. 7.2, the abrasive particle size does not enter explicitly; however, it is readily conceivable that the roughness factor tan θ might be size-dependent.   The experimental data just cited suggests that, with large abrasive particles, the shape of the abrasive indenters does not depend on the particle size, and consequently the overall wear rate is independent of particle size.

The reduction of wear rate when small particles are used has received a number of different explanations, which resolve themselves into two main categories, one being that with small particles the indenter geometry is different, the other suggesting that, with small abrasive particles, clogging of the system by abraded debris occurs.

Our own explanation is in the second category, and suggests that it is not so much the clogging of the abrasive (Fig. 7.7) which occurs, but the formation of large particles which prevent the abrasive from contacting the other surface (Fig. 7.14).   Such large particles arise from

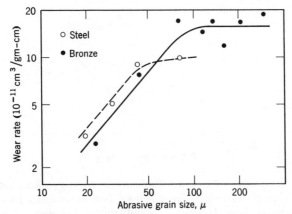

Fig. 7.13.   Wear rate of two metals as a function of abrasive grain size.

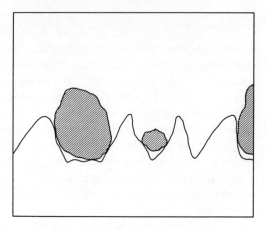

Fig. 7.14. Hypothetical abrasive surface in which large wear particles prevent abrasive action.

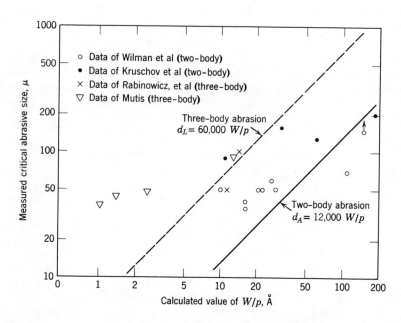

Fig. 7.15. Comparison of the critical abrasive size, for full abrasive action, with the W/p value for the material being abraded. Data is shown for two-body and three-body abrasion of metals, non-metals and lubricated surfaces.

the adhesive wear process, which takes place at the same time as abrasive action is occurring. These adhesive wear particles are potentially able to interfere with the abrasive action. From Chapter 6, we find that the size of *adherent* particles, which are those which interfere with abrasion of the *two-body* type, is of the order of 24,000 γ_a/p, whereas the size of *loose* particles, which can prevent *three-body* abrasion, is about 60,000 W_{ab}/p.

In Fig. 7.15 we show experimental data, for various materials, of the minimum abrasive particle size which gives full abrasive action, as a function of W_{ab}/p for these materials (for greater simplicity it is assumed that $W_{ab} = 2\gamma_a$). It will be seen that the data for three-body abrasion lie somewhat above the 60,000 W/p line, whereas the data for two-body abrasion lie similarly above the 12,000 W/p line. The fact that almost all the points lie above their corresponding lines is not important (apparently the size of the *largest* particles is important in this case, rather than the size of the *average* particles), but the obvious relation of the points to the lines suggests that our explanation for the "abrasive size effect" is correct.

7.6   Effect of Moisture Content of the Atmosphere, and of Lubrication, on Abrasive Wear

It has been observed that abrasive wear tests carried out in the summer give wear rates which are some 10 to 20% higher than those obtained in identical testing in the winter. This appears to be due to the effect of water vapor, since the humidity of laboratory air is much higher in summer than in winter. A careful series of runs made with controlled humidity gave results as shown in Fig. 7.16. It will be seen that humidity does have an effect, and that high humidity increases the wear rate by about 15%.

The closeness with which the experimental points lie on the line suggests that, when the humidity is controlled, abrasive wear data should be very reproducible (to within $\pm 2\%$). When the humidity is not controlled, variations in the wear rate of 10 to 20% are possible.

The mechanism by which the water vapor acts to affect the wear is elucidated by experiments in which various lubricating oils were applied to the sliding surfaces together with the abrasive. This increased the abrasive wear by factors of 2 to 4. The action of the lubricants appears to be that of flushing wear debris from the system more completely, thus increasing the effectiveness of the abrading action. It is known that water vapor can act as a lubricant on steel surfaces, although a poor one (Kingsbury and Rabinowicz, 1959);

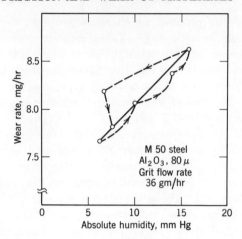

Fig. 7.16.   Wear rate as a function of humidity.   The arrows indicate the order of the tests.   When the humidity was suddenly reduced, the abrasive grains were still moist, hence an abnormally high wear rate resulted.

hence, its action is probably similar to that of the lubricating oil, but on a reduced scale.

7.7   Materials for Use in Abrasive Wear Situation

In this section we shall consider two types of materials, those to be used as abrasives when abrasive wear is to be encouraged, and those to be used as sliding materials when abrasive contaminants are present but abrasive wear is to be prevented.

Considering first the materials suitable for use as abrasives, we note that the desired criteria for good cutting action are hardness and sharpness.   The criterion of hardness means that the abrasive must be harder than the material it is to abrade, but it should be noted that, from the point of view of effective cutting action, the difference in hardness need not be enormous.   For example, if the abrasive is but 50% harder than the material to be abraded, it produces as great an abrasive wear rate as would a much harder abrasive.   If the abrasive is only a little harder than the material to be abraded, however, it tends more readily to have its sharp corners removed by plastic deformation and by abrasion, after which its own abrasive action is reduced.   Accordingly, it is advantageous to use a very hard abrasive, not to achieve a very high wear rate, but to maintain that wear rate for a very long period of time.

The second required property of an abrasive is that it be sharp. Accordingly, it is advantageous if the abrasive is brittle, so that it leaves sharp points and corners when it is put under high stress or when it is worn away. This criterion would favor a non-metal rather than a metal.

Both of these criteria suggest that hard non-metals are most suitable as abrasives, since these are the hardest materials known and tend to fail by brittle fracture. Indeed the common abrasives are all in this category. Aluminum oxide and silicon carbide, both of hardness above 2000 kg/mm^2, are the preferred materials for general use, since they combine the properties of extreme hardness, brittleness, and cheapness (Table 7.2). Existing materials of still greater hardness are boron carbide (2750 kg/mm^2) and diamond (8000 kg/mm^2), but the former is relatively expensive, whereas the latter is notoriously so.

For abrading relatively soft materials, for example wood, there is no need for extreme hardness. Garnet and sand (silica) are widely used in abrasive papers.

In the sandblasting process, the throughput of abrasive is quite large, so that deterioration of the abrasive is no problem. Hence sand is used to abrade metals (except the very hardest) as well as non-metals.

Hard metals are not generally used as abrasive particles, for reasons explained earlier, but they do find wide use in files. The maximum hardness of steel is about 1000 kg/mm^2, so that a hard steel file will cut soft metals, glass, and soft non-metals, but not, of course, hardened steel.

Table 7.2.   Materials for Use as Abrasives

Material	Composition	Hardness (kg/mm^2)
Diamond	C	8000
Boron carbide	B_4C	2750
Carborundum, silicon carbide	SiC	2500
Titanium carbide	TiC	2450
Corundum, alumina	Al_2O_3	2100
Zirconium carbide	ZrC	2100
Tungsten carbide	WC	1900
Garnet	$Al_2O_3.3FeO.3SiO_2$	1350
Zirconia	ZrO_2	1150
Quartz, silica, sand	SiO_2	800
Glass	Silicate	~500

When we come to the question of preventing abrasive action in sliding systems, the consideration of hardness is still foremost. The surfaces which are to resist abrasive wear must be harder than the contaminating particles. The most common contaminant is, naturally enough, the most common solid on earth, namely silica. This has a hardness which is almost as great as that attainable in metals, and thus there are a limited number of choices available for resisting abrasion by silica. These are outlined in Table 7.3.

In the design of sliding systems, it is helpful to be able to eliminate abrasive particles. This can sometimes best be done by filtering a circulating lubricant, but it is often augmented by having one hard and one soft sliding material, the function of the latter being that of collecting and burying any abrasive particles which get into the system. Typical soft bearing materials, commonly used in combination with hardened steel surfaces, are listed in Table 7.4.

Besides abrasive particles introduced from outside the sliding system, we must also consider the possibility of damage from wear particles produced during sliding. The softest of them are about as hard as the sliding surface from which they came; hence the soft material should have a hardness less than one-third that of the harder material, (Fig. 7.17). Table 7.4 shows that this rule is indeed obeyed in practice.

In considering the potential damage produced by these internally generated abrasive particles, we must note the size effect in abrasive wear (*cf*. Section 7.5). As long as the abrasive particles are small, the amount of damage they do is limited, not only when there is boundary lubrication and solid-solid contact occurs, but especially in fluid lubrication situations in which a film of substantial thickness separates the sliding surfaces most of the time. Accordingly, the danger which

Table 7.3.   Materials Resistant to Abrasion

Material	Hardness
Bearing steel	700–950 kg/mm^2
Tool steel	700–1000
Chromium (electroplated)	900
Carburized steel	900
Nitrided steel	900–1250
Tungsten carbide (cobalt binder)	1400–1800
Hard non-metal, or coating consisting of hard non-metal	See Table 7.2

Table 7.4. Recommended Soft Materials for Use in Journal
Bearings
(Data taken from Wilcock and Booser, 1957)

Bearing Material	Hardness	Minimum Shaft Hardness	Hardness Ratio
Lead-base babbitt	15–20 kg/mm^2	150	8
Tin-base babbitt	20–30	150	6
Alkali-hardened lead	22–26	200–250	9
Copper-lead	20–23	300	14
Silver (overplated)	25–50	300	8
Cadmium base	30–40	200–250	6
Aluminum alloy	45–50	300	6
Lead bronze	40–80	300	5
Tin bronze	60–80	300–400	5

must be guarded against primarily is the formation of really large
wear particles.

Large wear particles generally arise as result of surface fatigue fracture of materials which have either undergone a large number of stress
cycles or else were brittle to start with.   These factors argue in favor
of a metal with good fatigue properties, relatively immune to brittle

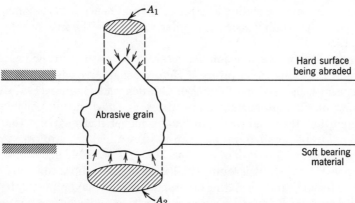

Fig. 7.17. Hypothetical appearance of an abrasive grain mounted in a soft bearing
material.   The geometry is such that A_2 will be greater than A_1 (say three times
as great), and then if the bearing material is less than $\frac{1}{3}$ as hard as the hard surface,
the grain will be pushed down into the bearing material.

fracture. In a sense, these requirements modify the high hardness requirements emphasized earlier in this section. In materials like the bearing steels, the highest hardness forms of the material (52100 steel at a Rockwell C level of 65 for example) have a fatigue limit which is no higher than that of the same material at a R_C level of 60 (Sachs, Sell, and Weiss, 1960), and are more brittle as well. And indeed, we have obse: ved very high abrasive wear rates in very hard, very brittle forms of steel. This results both from the ready formation of abrasive particles, and also from the fact that each particle tends to remove, as result of brittle fracture, material of volume larger than that given in eq. 7.1.

Before closing this discussion, we might remind the reader that just as brittle materials produce a wear volume greater than that given by eq. 7.1, so do highly elastic materials produce a wear volume which is much smaller than that indicated by eq. 7.1, because the deformation of the material by the abrasive is taken up elastically rather than by plastic deformation. Accordingly, highly elastic materials or elastometers (e.g., rubber), are frequently used in abrasive environments, and often out-perform much harder and stronger materials of more normal elastic strain limits (Selwood, 1961).

7.8 Polishing

Polishing is a special form of abrasive wear characterized by the use of very small abrasive grains (of order of magnitude five μ or less) on an elastic backing. Under these conditions abrasive wear rates per unit distance of sliding are quite low, and hence it is customary to use quite high sliding speeds, in order to increase the rate of wear per unit time.

The polishing phenomenon has received close study in the past, and there is an extensive literature. Here we shall cite a few of the chief conclusions, namely the finding of Bowden and Hughes (1937) that, in view of the high surface temperature attained during polishing, it is important for an abrasive to have a higher melting point than the material to be abraded, rather than to have a higher hardness at room temperature. The work of Samuels (1956) is valuable in showing that the polishing process is quite similar to ordinary abrasion, but on a reduced scale, and that the amorphous Beilby layer postulated by earlier workers (formed by successive melting and solidification of the surface layer) does not generally form.

An interesting feature of the polishing process is that, in view of the small size of each abrasive particle and because of its elastic backing, the total force on each particle is very small, being generally below the minimum size needed for the formation of wear particles. Accordingly, the ordinary processes of wear fragment formation are ruled out, but material is removed from high spots to low spots on the surface by some process not yet understood, but which appears to involve lateral displacement along the surface without the formation of free surface, thus leaving a relatively smooth surface. It is probably because of the presence of the minimum load effect, rather than because of surface melting or softening effects, that material is produced whose surface roughness is so much smaller than the equilibrium roughness normally attained during sliding.

Some recent experiments by Mr. Shiralkar in the Surface Laboratory at M.I.T. illustrate the fact that polishing is possible without any abrasive being present. In these tests a copper flat was pressed against a rotating wheel on which was mounted a fine mesh stainless steel screen with a rubber backing for greater resilience. Water was

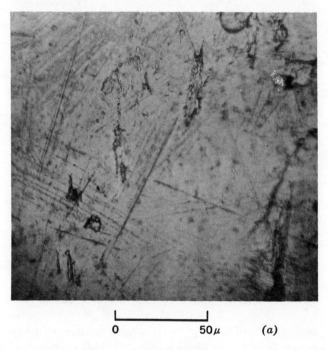

L_____I
0   50μ   (a)

Fig. 7.18a. Surface of copper block after sliding on water-lubricated stainless steel screen, 200 mesh, under a load of 5 gm. A smooth "polished" region is being produced.

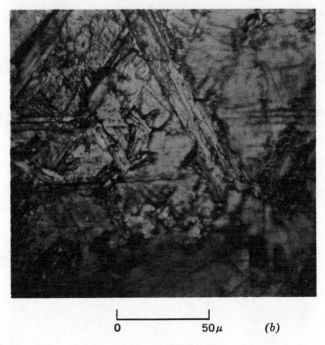

$$\vdash\!\!\!\!\!\rule{3cm}{0pt}\!\!\!\!\!\dashv$$
0   50μ   *(b)*

Fig. 7.18b. Surface of copper block after sliding on water-lubricated stainless steel screen, 100 mesh, under a load of 30 gm. The surface is very rough.

used to reduce the adhesive interaction between the copper and the screen mesh, but no abrasive was used. After about an hour, smooth "polished" regions appeared at the edges of the copper specimen (Fig. 7.18a). This polishing action was only obtained at light loads. At heavy loads, or with a coarse steel mesh, there was severe surface damage, and the copper surface became very rough (Fig. 7.18b).

7.9 Corrosive Wear

This form of wear occurs in situations in which the environment surrounding a sliding surface interacts chemically with it. If the products of reaction are worn off the surface, corrosive wear has occurred.

The phenomenon of corrosive wear is rather complex, and its quantitative analysis is still in its infancy (Burwell, 1957). We can however, analyze in a qualitative way the various processes that occur, and show how they influence the overall wear rate.

The first stage of corrosive wear is corrosive attack of the surface. This stage of the wear process is identical with that occurring in ordinary corrosion. When a naked surface (e.g., a metal) is exposed to an environment with which it can react, there is a rapid initial reaction, but the reaction slows down in time (Fig. 7.19). Associated with the slow-down is the formation of a coherent film on the surface, which separates the two reacting species more-or-less perfectly. For some combinations of materials and environments (e.g., aluminum in air) chemical reaction ceases completely after a certain thickness (for aluminum it is 2×10^{-6} cm) of reaction product has formed.

In some cases the chemical reaction keeps on going indefinitely at its initial rate (Fig. 7.20), either because no protective film is formed (it may be a liquid or gas, or dissolve in the liquid environment), or else because the film is porous, brittle, or spalls off. Under these circumstances the loss of material from the surface occurs at a rate essentially independent of any sliding which may occur, but which is determined by the characteristics of the corrosion process.

The second step of the corrosive wear process consists of the wearing away of the reaction product film, as result of the sliding which takes place. When this occurs, naked surface is exposed and corrosive attack continues.

In most cases, the corrosion products are harder and more brittle than the surfaces on which they form. There is a trend for the layer

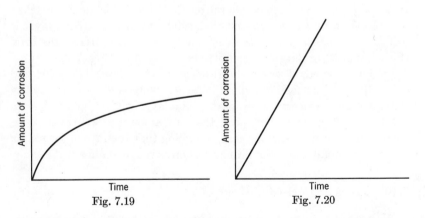

Fig. 7.19   Fig. 7.20

Fig. 7.19. Corrosion-time relation for a system in which a protective reaction product forms.
Fig. 7.20. Corrosion-time relation when no film forms, or else the film does not protect the surface.

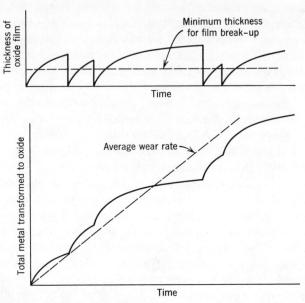

Fig. 7.21. Schematic illustration of corrosive wear process. It is assumed the oxide is brittle and comes off completely.

to be reasonably wear-resistant as long as it is thin, but for wear to become possible as soon as a certain thickness of layer is exceeded. How soon wear does in fact occur after the critical thickness is reached is determined by the conditions of the sliding process. If the layer is brittle, it may be assumed that, at any place on the surface, the total thickness of layer flakes off completely at one time (Fig. 7.21).

In those few cases where the reaction product layer is ductile and softer than the surface on which it forms, there is a high probability that, when wear occurs, only part of the layer will be removed (Fig. 7.22). It will be seen that, here, the total amount of wear will be far smaller than in the previous case, assuming that the rate of formation of reaction product and the probability of its removal remain the same.

7.10   Types of Corrosive Wear

We are now in a position to consider circumstances in which various forms of corrosive wear arise. The rampant form of corrosive wear, which is nothing but an example of ordinary corrosion, is seen in the "acid action" of an automobile, in which, when the engine is cold, sulfuric and sulfurous acids formed by the combustion of sulfur-containing ("sour") impurities in the gasoline react with the cast iron which constitutes cylinder walls of the engine. (Note that when the engine is hot the acids do not condense on the cylinder walls but on the muffler and tailpipe. Consequently, the corrosion occurs on these latter components).

Many other cases of this straight form of corrosion, in which the loss of material is but little affected by the sliding action, are seen in sliding systems in air at high temperature. Molybdenum alloys at 900°C, for example, form MoO_3, which is volatile and evaporates, thus allowing further corrosive attack. Boron carbide at 1000°C forms B_2O_3, which again is, at this temperature, quite volatile.

The formation of the second form of corrosive wear, involving the formation of brittle but adherent reaction products, is seen in most oxide-forming metals sliding in air, since most oxides are hard and brittle. The corrosive wear rate tends to be high only at elevated temperatures, since at lower temperatures not much reaction occurs, and the oxides are thin and thus less likely to break up.

Nonbrittle corrosion products on metal surfaces make up the third type of corrosive wear. These films consist primarily of metallic chlorides, sulfides, and phosphates. Most of these compounds are

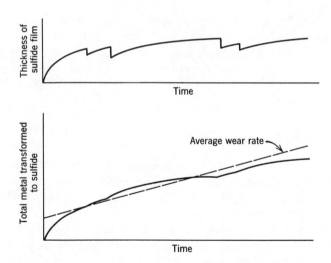

Fig. 7.22. Schematic illustration of corrosive wear process. It is assumed that the sulfide is sheared through without exposing naked metal. Note that wear rate is lower than in Fig. 7.21.

softer than the base metals on which they form.   Salts of fatty acids
(soaps) are also typical soft corrosive wear products.

Since soft corrosive reaction products may give quite low rates of
wear, as well as good lubrication characteristics (low friction, good
surface finish), conditions of sliding are often deliberately chosen so
that this type of corrosive wear occurs.   Metal cutting lubricants
often contain chlorine, sulfur, and phosphorus-containing additives
to encourage corrosive wear rather than the adhesive wear which
would otherwise occur, and gaseous hydrogen sulfide and halogenated
hydrocarbons are used for the same purpose (cf. the action of E. P.
lubricants).

7.11   Quantitative Aspects of Corrosive Wear

It is clear from Figs. 7.21 and 7.22 that, if we have a process in
which a film forms on the surfaces, this film being removed continuously during sliding, the rate of wear at each pass must be smaller than
the film thickness.   Since film thicknesses are typically of the order of
10^{-6} cm, and since the junction diameter may be assumed to be
10^{-3} cms, we may apply eq. 6.10, namely

$$\text{Depth worn away } (h) = \frac{k}{3} \times \text{distance slid } (x)$$

If we substitute $h = 10^{-6}$ or less, and $x = 10^{-3}$, we obtain $k = 3.10^{-3}$
as a maximum wear rate.   Perhaps $k = 10^{-4}$ to 10^{-5} might be typical
values in practice, these being less than for unlubricated sliding, but
greater than for surfaces covered by an effective boundary lubricant.

Naturally the rampant corrosion case cannot be analyzed in this
way, since no film is formed.

7.12   Surface Fatigue Wear

Two types of fracture wear are common.   The first is that observed
in rolling applications, namely gears and rolling contact bearings, and
the second is observed in brittle, ceramic materials under rolling or
sliding conditions.

The first of these, generally referred to as surface fatigue wear, is of
great practical importance in that it constitutes the main mode of
failure of rolling contact elements.   This form of wear is closely related
to the general phenomenon of fatigue of materials, in that there is a
characteristic interrelation between the stresses in the contacting materials and the number of cycles required to produce fracture, and super-

posed on this interrelationship there are very marked statistical fluctuations.

In a typical application, the contacting components are given a very good surface finish so that the deformation under the applied normal loading is elastic rather than plastic. As operation of the mechanism occurs, the interaction at the interface consists primarily of rolling motion, with often a small ($\sim$1%) superposed component of sliding. The temperature is usually quite moderate (under 200°F), and oil or grease lubrication is provided. Under these circumstances adhesive, abrasive, and corrosive wear are virtually absent, and motion can continue for long periods of time (e.g., millions of revolutions) without substantial changes of the surface configuration.

As operation of the mechanism continues, stressing and unstressing of the material in the rolling track continues to take place. For a long time the material appears to be quite unaffected by this stress cycling, but suddenly, perhaps after many thousand hours of operation, a particle spalls off the surface, and thereafter deterioration of the surface and flaking off of fragments becomes rapid.

The characteristics of the fatigue wear process are as follows:

1. The particles which are removed tend to be large, that is, their dimensions appear to be closer to those of the area of contact under stress (order of magnitude 1000 μ), rather than the characteristic adhesive wear particle size for the material (order of magnitude 30 μ).

2. Surface-active lubricants generally lower the life of the unit considerably, as compared to operation with low-additive petroleum oil (Reichenbach, 1962). The presence of these liquids *lowers* the life by about a factor of 10, whereas, under adhesive wear conditions, these lubricants might *raise* the useful life by factors of about 100.

3. The life is markedly load dependent, the relationship generally being of the type

$$t = \frac{\text{constant}}{L^3} \qquad (7.5)$$

where t is the time to failure and L the load. Since for elastic deformation of spherically ended contacting materials the maximum stress varies as the cube root of the load, we may write eq. 7.5 in the form

$$t = \frac{\text{constant}}{\sigma_m{}^9} \qquad (7.6)$$

where σ_m is the maximum elastic stress.

4. The life is subject to enormous experimental scatter, and varia-

tion in life by factors of 200 to 1 under apparently identical conditions are not uncommon. It should be noted that, under adhesive wear conditions, the scatter, while quite large, is generally only about a factor of 10.

Many of the characteristic features of surface fatigue wear are quite similar to those observed in fatigue testing of bulk specimens. The general principle, that the cumulative application of stress cycles, where each stress individually is well within the elastic limit, can cause a material to fail by fracture, is common to both situations. The fact that the life varies inversely as a high power of the stress, about 9 for surface fatigue wear and also about 9 for general fatigue (within the limits of 10^3 to 10^6 stress cycles) is another point of similarity, as is the fact that a surface-active environment has an effect on shortening the life by approximately a factor of 10. (The influence of environment on mechanical properties of materials was first established by Rehbinder, 1931. Unfortunately, the effect of atmosphere, which changes oxide properties etc., is so important and variable, that the reproducibility of the Rehbinder effect is notoriously poor).

The two important differences between ordinary fatigue and surface fatigue are, first, that the fluctuations in the life are much more severe in the rolling contact situation, being a factor of more than 100 as against a factor of 10 in the bulk case. Second, there is the important phenomenon of fatigue limit stress which is observed in ordinary bulk testing, in consequence of which there exists a stress (usually between one-third and one-half the yield stress) below which a material enjoys an infinite fatigue life. No such limit exists in the surface fatigue case. It will be appreciated that both these differences make it more difficult to design rolling contact elements for predictable long life at reasonably high stress loading. Thus we are unable to design rolling contact

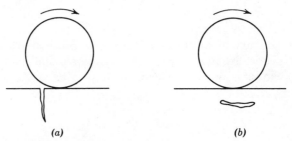

(a)   (b)

Fig. 7.23.   Appearance of typical surface fatigue failures in their early stages. (a) Surface crack; (b) subsurface crack.

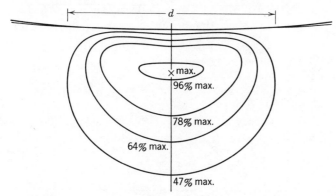

Fig. 7.24. Position of stress maximum for elastic contact of sphere and flat (Davies, 1949).

elements whose contact stresses are below some definite value and gain the assurance that we have eliminated fatigue failure.   Furthermore, if we do happen to know the conditions under which (say) 90% of a group of identical rolling contact elements will meet specifications, it becomes very difficult to decide on measures to be taken to increase the survival rate to 99.99%.

The experimental study of surface fatigue wear is rather difficult. Until spalling occurs there are few useful observations that can be made, although some investigators have made metallographic studies of rolling contact materials and discovered that the crack which initiates spalling is sometimes located at the surface, at other times below the surface (Fig. 7.23).   The occurrence of subsurface cracks is probably related to the fact that the point with maximum shear stress and hence the point with the maximum tendency for plastic yielding is located a small distance below the surface (Fig. 7.24).

The main experimental investigations of surface fatigue wear have consisted of running rolling contact devices until spalling occurs, and noting the time to spalling.   In view of the statistical variations it becomes necessary to run a large number of repeat tests, of nominally identical rolling contact elements.   These tests are plotted on a Weibull diagram, in which the abscissa is a function of the rank of the failed element and the ordinate is the log of the time to failure (Weibull, 1951).   In most cases the points on a Weibull plot give a straight line (Fig. 7.25), and from it we may read off the time interval at which 10%, 50%, etc. of the elements would fail under the imposed test conditions.

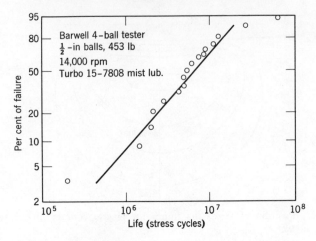

Fig. 7.25. Typical Weibull plot (courtesy of W. D. Syniuta).

Where fatigue wear is a problem, it is generally alleviated by improving the quality of the bearing steel (e.g., by vacuum melting, by reducing inclusions, by eliminating austenite which is unstable and tends to change to martensite), or reducing the loading. Almost nothing is known about the problem of reducing the scatter between repeat runs. This is a very important problem, since in many applications it is vital to be able to eliminate early failures.

7.13 Brittle Fracture Wear

The other form of fracture wear is that which occurs in brittle materials (e.g., glass, sintered ceramic, etc.). During sliding, a characteristic series of cracks is observed in the wear track (Fig. 7.26). Subsequently, large wear particles tend to be produced as result of the surface breakup.

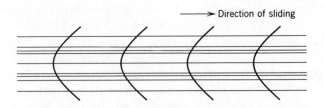

Fig. 7.26. Characteristic appearance of wear track of brittle material showing tensile cracks.

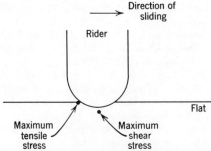

Fig. 7.27. Schematic illustration showing the position of maximum tensile stress behind the region of contact. In brittle materials, cracking may be produced there.

There has been very little study of this brittle fracture form of wear. The wear rate is usually quite high (wear constant higher than 10^{-3}), and rather variable, depending on the exact way the specimen was produced. The wear seems to become especially high for materials whose tensile strength is less than one-third their compressive, which appears to be due to the fact that, the maximum tensile stress behind a typical junction is about one-third the compressive stress under the junction (Fig. 7.27). Clearly the compressive stress is of order of magnitude of σ_y, and if the tensile stress is less than $\sigma_y/3$, tensile failure will take place behind the junction.

The foregoing discussion implies, not only that very brittle materials are subject to poor wear behavior, but also that somewhat less brittle materials show fairly good wear properties. Thus chrome plate, sintered alumina, and in fact many of the ceramic composite types of material are too brittle for most structural applications, but perform satisfactorily under sliding conditions. For structural applications it is generally desirable that the material is capable of some plastic yielding under tensile loading, so that stress concentrations do not lead to failure. This implies that the tensile strength will be as great as the compressive strength. For sliding applications it is necessary merely that the tensile strength is greater than one-third the compressive strength.

References

Aleinikov, F. K. (1957a), The Influence of Abrasive Powder Microhardness on the Values of the Coefficients of Volume Removal, *Soviet Physics–Technical Physics*, **2**, 505–511.

Aleinikov, F. K. (1957b), The Effect of Certain Physical and Mechanical Properties on the Grinding of Brittle Materials, *Soviet Physics—Technical Physics*, **2**, 2529–2538.

Avient, B. W. E., J. Goddard, and M. Wilman (1960), An Experimental Study of Friction and Wear during Abrasion of Metals, *Proc. Roy. Soc.*, A **258**, 159–180.

Bowden, F. P., and T. P. Hughes (1937), Polishing, Surface Flow, and the Formation of the Beilby Layer, *Proc. Roy. Soc.*, A **160**, 575–587.

Burwell, J. T. (1957), Survey of Possible Wear Mechanisms, *Wear*, **1**, 119–141.

Davies, R. M. (1949), The Determination of Static and Dynamic Yield Stresses using a Steel Ball, *Proc. Roy. Soc.*, A **197**, 416–432.

Goddard, J., and M. Wilman (1962), A Theory of Friction and Wear during the Abrasion of Metals, *Wear*, **5**, 114–135.

Kingsbury, E. P., and E. Rabinowicz (1959), Friction and Wear of Metals to 1000°C, *Trans. Amer. Soc. Mech. Eng.*, **81 D**, 118–121.

Kruschov, M. M. (1957), Resistance of Metals to Wear by Abrasion, as Related to Hardness, pp. 655–659 of *Proc. Conf. Lubrication and Wear*, Institution Mech. Eng., London.

Kruschov, M. M., and M. A. Babichev (1956), An Investigation of the Wear of Metals and Alloys on an Abrasive Surface, pp. 1–12 of *Friction and Wear in Machinery*, Vol. 11, A.S.M.E., New York.

Kruschov, M. M., and M. A. Babichev (1958), Resistance to Abrasive Wear of Structurally Inhomogeneous Materials, pp. 5–23 of *Friction and Wear in Machinery*, Vol. 12, A.S.M.E., New York.

Kruschov, M. M., and M. A. Babichev (1960), *Investigations into the Wear of Metals* (in Russian), U.S.S.R. Academy of Sciences, Moscow.

Lopa, M. (1956), *A Study of the Influence of Hardness, Rubbing Speed and Load on Abrasive Wear*, B.S. Thesis in Mechanical Engineering, M.I.T. Cambridge, Mass.

Mulhearn, T. O., and L. E. Samuels (1962), The Abrasion of Metals: A Model of the Process, *Wear*, **5**, 478–498.

Mutis-Valdivieso, A (1964), *Influence of Lubrication on the Critical Abrasive Particle Size*, M.S. Thesis in Mechanical Engineering, M.I.T. Cambridge, Mass.

Rabinowicz, E., L. A. Dunn, and P. G. Russell (1961a), The Abrasive Wear Resistance of Some Bearing Steels, *Lubrication Engineering*, **17**, 587–593.

Rabinowicz, E., L. A. Dunn, and P. G. Russell (1961b), A Study of Abrasive Wear under Three-Body Conditions, *Wear*, **4**, 345–355.

Rehbinder, M. (1931), Diminution of Scratch Hardness through Adsorption of Surfactive Substances (in German), *Z. Physik*, **72**, 191–205.

Reichenbach, G. S. (1962), Fatigue, Chapter 17 of *An Introduction to the Mechanical Behavior of Materials*, F. A. McClintock and A. S. Argon, eds., M.I.T., Cambridge, Mass.

Sachs, G., R. Sell, and V. Weiss (1960), Tension, Compression and Fatigue Properties of Several SAE 52100 and Tool Steels used in Ball Bearings, *N.A.S.A. Tech. Note D-239.*

Samuels, L. E. (1956), The Nature of Mechanically Polished Surfaces: The Surface Deformation Produced by the Abrasion and Polishing of 70:30 Brass, *J. Inst. Met.*, **85**, 51–62.

Selwood, A. (1961), The Abrasion of Materials by Carborundum Paper, *Wear*, **4**, 311–318.

Spurr, R. T., and T. P. Newcomb (1957), The Friction and Wear of Various

Materials Sliding against Unlubricated Surfaces of Different Types and Degrees of Roughness, pp. 269–275 of *Proc. Conf. Lubrication and Wear,* Institution of Mechanical Engineers, London.

Tabor, D. (1951), *The Hardness of Metals,* Oxford University Press, Oxford.

Tabor, D. (1954), Mohs Hardness Scale—A Physical interpretation, *Proc. Phys. Soc. (London),* B **67,** 249–257.

Toporov, G. V. (1958), "The Influence of Structure on the Abrasive Wear of Cast Iron," pp. 39–59 of *Friction and Wear in Machinery,* Vol. 12, A.S.M.E., New York.

Weibull, W. (1951), A Statistical Distribution Function of Wide Range of Applicability, *J. Appl. Mech.,* **18,** 293–297.

Wilcock, D. F., and E. R. Booser (1957), *Bearing Design and Application,* McGraw-Hill, New York.

8

Lubrication

8.1 Introduction

In previous chapters we have on a number of occasions shown that lubricants can drastically change the friction and wear characteristics of sliding systems. In this chapter we shall examine their mode of action systematically. There are a number of definitions extant on what constitutes a lubricant, but the most general and probably best definition is that a lubricant is a substance which is capable of altering the nature of the surface interaction between contacting solids.

The term "lubrication" is applied to two different situations. *Fluid lubrication* occurs when a thick film of some liquid or gas completely separates two solids. Since the phenomena of fluid lubrication are governed by the mechanical properties of the fluid, they fall outside the scope of this book. We shall be concerned here with the case of *boundary lubrication*, where the lubricant forms a thin film of the order of magnitude of one monolayer, interposed between the contacting surfaces.

Another type of lubrication, closely related to boundary lubrication, arises when a soft solid film, which may be of substantial thickness, is interposed between the sliding surfaces. This is generally referred to as *solid film lubrication*. The situation, where the solid film arises as result of a chemical reaction between the sliding surface and its environment, is sometimes referred to as *E. P. lubrication*.

Most lubricants are introduced into a sliding system with the aim of reducing the amount of interaction between the contacting surfaces. Thus a lubricant may be used to reduce the friction force, or the

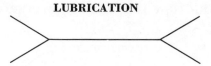

Fig. 8.1.   An unlubricated junction.

amount of wear, or the degree of surface adhesion.   Sometimes, however, the prime task of the lubricant is to reduce the interfacial temperature, which otherwise might produce some harmful change, for example melting, in one of the contacting materials.   In some specialized applications, for example metal cutting, the task of the lubricant may be to influence the way that chips are formed, or the nature of the surface finish.   In a few applications, those concerned with the wearing-in of mechanisms, it is the function of a special wearing-in lubricant to produce fast wear during running-in, after which the lubricant is removed, and a more normal lubricant substituted.

The mode of action of lubricants may be best understood by considering the appearance of a typical junction.   In Fig. 8.1, we show the appearance of the unlubricated junction.   When a lubricant is applied, it may form a surface layer which separates the surfaces completely (Fig. 8.2), or else it may act over part of the junction but not over some other part (Fig. 8.3), or it may be present as an incomplete layer over the whole interface (Fig. 8.4).   The complete separation of the surfaces (Fig. 8.2) is characteristic of effective solid film lubrication, but hardly ever occurs during boundary lubrication.   In boundary lubrication, the incomplete layer of Fig. 8.4 probably occurs most

Fig. 8.2.   A solid-film lubricated junction.

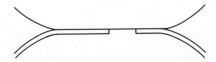

Fig. 8.3.   A boundary lubricated junction showing partial breakthrough.

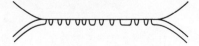

Fig. 8.4.   A boundary lubricated junction showing incomplete coverage.

often.   This type of behavior is hard to analyze, however, so that discussion of boundary lubrication is generally based on the two-step
model of Fig. 8.3.   This model has given surprisingly useful results,
as we shall see.

8.2   Solid Film Lubrication

First, we may consider the case where a solid layer separates the
materials completely at the interface.   Examples of this phenomenon
would be cases where a solid film was deliberately applied, for example,
a thin layer of electroplated lead on a metal surface, or a layer consisting of molybdenum disulfide particles incorporated in an epoxy
resin and baked on to a solid surface.   Alternatively, the layer might
be formed by chemical reaction, for example, an oxide layer on a metal
surface, formed as result of reaction with the metal of oxygen from the
air.   Another typical layer of chemical origin might be a sulfide or a
chloride film formed by the reaction with the metal surface of sulfur- or
chlorine-containing compounds contained in a liquid carrier applied to
the surfaces, or in the gaseous environment surrounding the surfaces.·
In some cases, of course, the solid film is readily broken up during
sliding (Fig. 8.5).   This is particularly true of some of the oxides,
which tend to be brittle materials, far less able to undergo elastic or
plastic deformation than are their metallic substrates.   Even if the
layer is not broken up, it may be so strong that it cannot be sheared
during sliding, so that shear occurs in the bulk material on either side
of the interface (Fig. 8.6).   In either case, the layer does not change
the frictional properties of the sliding materials, so that the equation

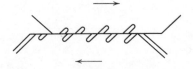

Fig. 8.5.   Solid film hard and brittle—broken up.

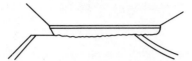

Fig. 8.6.   Solid film strong—shear occurs outside film.

for the friction coefficient can be written in the form

$$f_m = \frac{s_m}{p_m} \tag{8.1}$$

where s_m is the shear strength of the softer bulk material, and p_m is its hardness, just as if the layer had been absent.   (*Note:* the subscript m used in this chapter denotes that we are considering the property of an unlubricated *material*).

A solid film, however, even if hard and brittle, may become of significance in situations where the interaction between the contacting materials is strong.   In the absence of the surface layer, the friction may be very high (eq. 4.8), in accordance with the relation

$$f_m = \left(\frac{s_m}{p_m}\right) \left\{ 1 + \frac{2W_{ab} \cot \theta}{p_m r} + \cdots \right\} \tag{8.2}$$

but the presence of the solid layer reduces W_{ab} and hence reduces the friction.   The layer influences the friction by preventing the growth of the junction under the adhesive attraction of the two surfaces. Thus the layer reduces the area of contact which must be sheared during sliding.

Where the solid film is soft, it will influence the frictional behavior in a very direct way, since shear will take place either across the film (Fig. 8.7) or between the film and the other surface (Fig. 8.8).   In the

Fig. 8.7.   Solid film sheared through.

Fig. 8.8.   Shear occurs at solid film's periphery.

first case the friction coefficient will be given by

$$f_l = \frac{s_l}{p_m} \tag{8.3}$$

where s_l is the shear strength of the lubricant film, and p_m is, as before, the bulk hardness of the contacting material. (*Note:* the subscript l denotes presence of an unbroken *lubricant film*). Since s_l must be less than s_m, the shear strength of the contacting material itself (or else we would not regard the solid film as being "soft"), it is clear that the friction f_l of the lubricated film is less than that of the unlubricated film f_m in the ratio of s_l to s_m, that is,

$$\frac{f_l}{f_m} = \frac{s_l}{s_m} \tag{8.4}$$

Where shear takes place between the film and the other surface (Fig. 8.8), the friction can be no greater than the value given in eq. 8.3 (or else shear would take place across the film), and the friction is usually not much smaller, so that we again get a reduction in friction, compared to the unlubricated case, of magnitude nearly equal to that indicated in eq. 8.4.

8.3 Boundary Lubrication—the Single Penetration Model

We now proceed to consider the case where the lubricating layer is only of molecular thickness, and hence is readily penetrated during sliding. When considering an interface covered by a penetrated lubricant layer, we shall consider two possible extremes, first, that where the lubricant layer is penetrated at one point only (Fig. 8.3), and second, where the lubricant layer is penetrated at very many points of limited area (Fig. 8.4), and consider their consequences.

If the lubricant layer is penetrated at one point only, we have a simple two-component system in which there is solid-solid contact over one fraction of the junction, which fraction we denote by α, and solid film lubrication over the rest of the junction, of proportion $(1 - \alpha)$. The shear strength for the solid-solid contact regime is s_m, that of the solid film regime is s_l, and hence the force required to shear the junction of area A will be (Bowden, Gregory, and Tabor, 1945).

$$F = \alpha A s_m + (1 - \alpha)A s_l \tag{8.5}$$

Combining this with the eq. 3.2 for the junction area

$$L = p_m A$$

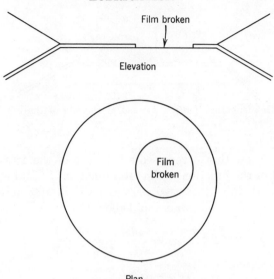

Film broken

Elevation

Film broken

Plan

Fig. 8.9. Elevation and plan view of hypothetical junction showing circular breakthrough area.

results in the relation

$$f = \frac{F}{L} = \frac{\alpha s_m}{p_m} + \frac{(1 - \alpha)s_l}{p_m}$$

We eliminate the terms s_m/p_m and s_l/p_m using eq. 8.1 and 8.3 respectively, and obtain

$$f = \alpha f_m + (1 - \alpha)f_l \qquad (8.6)$$

An important consequence of the two-component approach to boundary lubrication is that it enables us to calculate the wear produced by boundary-lubricated surfaces, if we assume that the area of breakthrough is circular (like the junction itself) (Fig. 8.9), that the particle produced is hemispherical (like that produced by the unlubricated junction) (Fig. 8.10), and that the probability of producing a particle is the same for the penetrated part of the junction in the lubricated case as it is for the junction as a whole in the unlubricated case. It may be assumed that no wear whatever is attributable to that part of the junction covered by the lubricant. Then we have

$$\frac{\text{Wear lubricated}}{\text{Wear unlubricated}} = \beta = \frac{\pi d^3/12}{\pi d_m{}^3/12} = \frac{d^3}{d_m{}^3} \qquad (8.7)$$

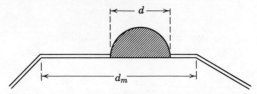

Fig. 8.10.   Hemispherical particle formed at the site of the breakthrough area.

Also, we know that α represents the ratio of the area of the penetrated part of the junction to the total junction.   Making the assumption that both the penetrated part and the total junction are semi-
circles, we have (Rabinowicz and Tabor, 1951)

$$\alpha = \frac{\pi d^2/4}{\pi d_m{}^2/4} = \frac{d^2}{d_m{}^2} \qquad (8.8)$$

$$\therefore \beta = \alpha^{3/2} \qquad (8.9)$$

It will be seen that this assumption of penetration at one point has
led to a simple equation for the drop in friction and the drop in wear.
These equations may be tested experimentally in a number of ways, as
we shall now proceed to show.

Equation 8.6 is best tested by checking frictional behavior at two
different sliding speeds.   It is known that f_m and f_l vary with speed,
and it may be assumed that α, the fraction making solid contact, is
independent of speed.   Then if we denote the friction at one speed by
f', and that at the other by f'', we have

$$f' - f'_l = \alpha(f'_m - f'_l)$$
$$f'' - f''_l = \alpha(f''_m - f''_l)$$

When we eliminate α, we obtain

$$(f' - f'_l)(f''_m - f''_l) = (f'' - f''_l)(f'_m - f'_l) \qquad (8.10)$$

This equation is a linear relation between the two variable quantities,
f' and f''.   Hence if α is varied, and tests at two different velocities are
made for each value of α, the friction coefficient obtained at the two
velocities will be linearly related, in accord with eq. 8.10.   Figure 8.11
shows the result of an experiment in which tests were carried out at
one sliding speed and friction coefficients were measured at various
points along a circular track, and then a repeat test over the same
track was carried out at a different sliding speed, after which a point-
by-point comparison of friction coefficients was carried out.   In this

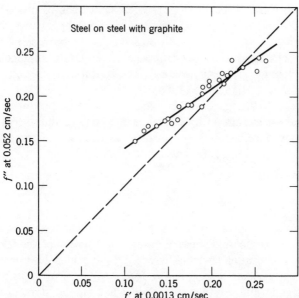

Fig. 8.11. Comparison of f at two velocities, utilizing natural variation in α along sliding track.

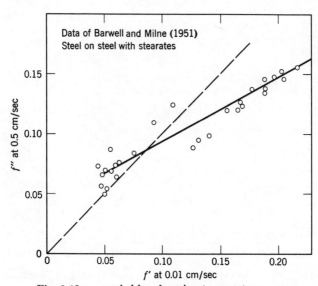

Fig. 8.12. α varied by changing temperature.

case the intrinsic variations of α, as a result of variations of lubricant adhesion, were utilized. Figure 8.12 shows the results of an experiment in which α was varied by varying the temperature, thus producing partial desorption. It will be seen that in both cases the data do lie very closely on two straight lines. A closely analogous check of eq. 8.6, using copper surfaces ozidized to different degrees, is outlined by Tamai and Rightmire (1965).

Equation 8.9, regarding the reduction in wear produced by a lubricant, is best evaluated by carrying out tests of unlubricated surfaces and of surfaces covered by various lubricants, and then plotting the wear as a function of the friction.

We have

$$\beta^{\frac{2}{3}} (= \alpha) = \frac{f - f_l}{f_m - f_l} \tag{8.11}$$

Figure 8.13 shows a plot of the $\frac{2}{3}$ power of the wear rate reduction β (compared to the unlubricated case) as a function of the friction coefficient, for titanium surfaces covered by various lubricants, each of which has associated with it a different value of α. Again the points fit a straight line quite well. Somewhat similar data are shown by Nagata, Tomoda, and Haga (1956).

The relationship of eq. 8.11 is very important in that it suggests that the effect of a lubricant on the wear will be much greater than its effect

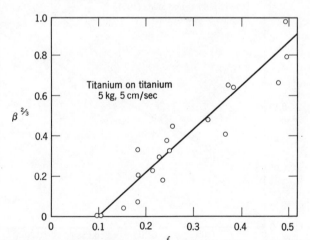

Fig. 8.13. The $\frac{2}{3}$ power of the ratio of wear to that of unlubricated sliding, plotted as a function of the friction.

on the friction. Thus, if $f_m = 0.6$ and $f_l = 0.05$, a factor-of-two change in friction coefficient from 0.12 to 0.06 will produce a factor-of-twenty change in the wear.

8.4 Boundary Lubrication—The (Alternative) Multiple Penetration Model

Having considered in some detail the single penetration model (Fig. 8.3) and worked out its consequences, we now turn to the multiple penetration model (Fig. 8.4) and attempt to evaluate the effect that a lubricant layer of this type will have on the friction and wear.

As regards the friction, it is likely, but by no means certain, that the friction coefficient will still be linearly related to the friction coefficients for the fully lubricated (f_l) and the unlubricated (f_m) sliding conditions, even though the linear extent of each little clean or lubricated region has become so small that continuum mechanics can no longer be applied. If we make the assumption that the two component formula of eq. 8.6, namely,

$$f = \alpha f_m + (1 - \alpha)f_l$$

is correct, or at any rate approximately, we can use the measured friction coefficient to provide an estimate of α.

When we turn to wear, however, we must now completely change our model of wear particle formation and our equations for the amount of wear. We have to abandon the requirement that the particle size is related to the size of unlubricated patches at the interface, because these patches are now very small, perhaps of molecular dimensions. Furthermore, if the interface is contaminated, the probability k that a wear particle is formed may be quite different from the corresponding probability k_m in the unlubricated case. We can get an idea, however, of the size of the wear particles by introducing the concept of surface energy. We assume that the energy of adhesion of the uncontaminated contact is W_m, given by

$$W_m = \gamma_a + \gamma_b - \gamma_{ab} \tag{8.12}$$

where γ_a and γ_b are the surface energies of the two unlubricated surfaces and γ_{ab} the interfacial energy (eq. 2.13). Further, we postulate that the energy of adhesion of the fully contaminated region is W_l, namely

$$W_l = \gamma_1 + \gamma_2 - \gamma_{1,2} \tag{8.13}$$

when γ_1 and γ_2 are the surface energies of the lubricant layers on the two surfaces and $\gamma_{1,2}$ their interfacial energy. Then we might write the surface energy W of the actual, partially contaminated, interface in the form

$$W = \alpha W_m + (1 - \alpha)W_l \qquad (8.14)$$

If the diameter of the wear particle is assumed proportional to W, and this seems a reasonable assumption (compare eq. 6.23), we have for the diameter of the lubricated particle d as compared to that of the unlubricated particle d_m,

$$\frac{d}{d_m} = \frac{W}{W_m} = \frac{\alpha W_m + (1 - \alpha)W_l}{W_m} = \alpha + \frac{(1 - \alpha)W_l}{W_m} \qquad (8.15)$$

This relation differs quite drastically from that obtained according to the two component model (eq. 8.9), namely,

$$\frac{d}{d_m} = \alpha^{\frac{1}{2}} \qquad (8.16)$$

and this difference is most pronounced when α is very small. Indeed, in the limit, namely when α is zero, the two-component model suggests that there are no wear particles (or, which is the same thing, that there are wear particles of zero size), whereas the uniform contamination model gives particles of dimensions $W_l d_m / W_m$.

We may apply one fundamental test to the uniform contamination model and its eq. 8.15, namely that the same distance d should always be obtained with the same lubricant and the same surfaces, even under somewhat different experimental conditions.

In our laboratory we have used three quite distinct ways to measure d. In the first of these, copper surfaces were slid in the presence of various lubricants, and the size of the wear particles was measured directly (Rabinowicz and Foster, 1964). In the second test, copper chips produced by a metal cutting process were placed in a ball mill, a lubricant was added, and the ball mill was operated for a week, until an equilibrium particle size as postulated by Huttig and Sales (1956) was attained (Tyagi, 1963). The third test consisted in sliding one copper surface on another for a number of hours in the presence of a lubricant (Finkin, 1962). It may be shown that, if the sliding geometry is suitable, an equilibrium surface roughness is attained and the peak-to-trough roughness corresponds to the wear particle size for the same sliding combination (Rabinowicz and Foster, 1963).

The data obtained in these tests are shown in Table 8.1, and it will be seen that the three methods give substantially similar results. The least reliable method is that involving loose wear particles, since in the

Table 8.1. Distance Factors d for Lubricated Copper Surfaces

Surface Condition	Wear Particle Diameter	Peak-to-Trough Roughness	Ball-Milled Particle Diameter
No lubricant	177μ	75μ	125μ
Cetane	12	12	12
Silicone DC 200	9.5	9.0	7.0
Ucon fluid LB-70X	9.5	4.0	—
Palmitic acid in cetane	8.0	4.5	5.5

unlubricated condition there is a load effect (Fig. 6.22), whereas with some of the lubricants the formation of a frictional polymer (often nicknamed "black gunk") occurs, as result of the catalytic action of the naked metal surface and the lubricant molecules (Hermance and Egan, 1958; Campbell and Lee, 1962). This frictional polymer later clogs the filters used in the sieving procedure and thus interferes with the particle size measurements.

From the data of Table 8.1, we may compute d by means of eq. 6.23, and these values are shown in Table 8.2, as is the friction coefficient which we have obtained with the same combinations. It will be seen that there is a good correlation between the computed value of surface energy and the measured value of friction coefficient, suggesting that a low surface energy is indeed an indication of good lubrication.

For copper surfaces lubricated by palmitic acid in cetane, we might anticipate a value of W of 50 erg/cm^2, since the surface energy of fatty acids and their derivatives (e.g., a soap film) is about 25 erg/cm^2. The actual value of W, namely 100 erg/cm^2, is of the same order of

Table 8.2. Comparison of Surface Energy of Adhesion and Friction; Copper Surfaces

Lubricant	Distance Factor (from Table 8.1)	Surface Energy (Computed)	Friction Coefficient (Measured)
None	100μ	2000 erg/cm^2	1.3
Cetane	12	240	0.35
Silicone DC 200	9	180	0.25
Ucon fluid LB-70X	7	140	0.15
Palmitic acid in cetane	5	100	0.10

magnitude as the expected value, but rather higher, and this may indicate a value of α in eq. 8.14 of about $2\frac{1}{2}\%$.

It should be noted that, although the uniform contamination model gives useful information on the size of wear particles, it does not yield values for the total amount of wear. This is because there appears to be no way of estimating the probability k that a particle of diameter d will be formed at the junction, although it seems likely that k will be less than k_m, the corresponding probability in the unlubricated case. The two-component model does provide an estimate of the wear rate (eq. 8.9), and this agrees well with practice (Fig. 8.13). Perhaps the correct model would lie somewhere between the two extremes which we have considered.

We might conclude our discussion of the continuous contamination model with the comment that this somewhat different approach to lubrication is inherently plausible, and that it gives results which rank common lubricants in the correct order. The concept of surface energy is also successful in explaining such anomalous effects as the rather effective lubrication of titanium by short-chain molecules like methyl di-iodide (Rabinowicz, 1958), whereas the two-phase model predicts incorrectly that a short-chain compound should be poor, and a long-chain material like stearic acid should be preferable. Furthermore, the continuous contamination model can explain more readily the fact that boundary lubricated contacts have an electric resistance which is hardly greater than that of similar unlubricated contacts.

The important difference between the two models lies in their attitude toward the real function of the lubricant. Is it to form a thick film which separates the sliding surfaces, or is it to lower the energy of adhesion (Levine and Zisman, 1957)? Critical experiments to decide the question are presently lacking.

8.5 Properties of Lubricants and Materials—Temperature

It has been found that lubricants cannot be divided into absolute classes like very good, fairly good, poor, etc., but rather, that each lubricant tends to be useful under certain sliding conditions, and much less useful under others. Of the imposed variables which influence the sliding conditions, by far the most important is the surface temperature.

If we take a pure chemical substance like steryl alcohol $CH_3 \cdot (CH_2)_{17} \cdot OH$, apply it to a typical metal such as copper, and monitor the friction coefficient and the wear rate as a function of temperature, we get the plot shown in Fig. 8.14. It will be seen that at

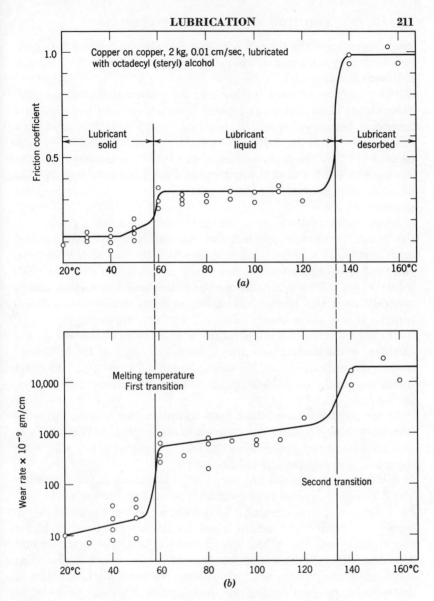

Fig. 8.14. (*a*) Friction as a function of temperature. (*b*) Metal transfer as a function of temperature.

low temperatures the friction and wear are low, at intermediate temperatures they are medium, whereas at high temperatures both friction and wear are very high.

The transition between the low and the intermediate sliding conditions occurs quite sharply at a point generally referred to as the first transition temperature, and it has been found that this often corresponds closely to the melting temperature of the lubricant. At temperatures below the first transition, the lubricant is present on the surface as a solid, and thus functions as a solid film lubricant (α close to zero), whereas above the melting point of the lubricant α takes on a sizeable value.

As the temperature is raised above the first transition temperature, the liquid lubricant is held less and less tightly to the solid surface, until eventually a point is reached at which the two sliding surfaces can push the lubricant aside completely and establish effective solid-solid contact. This point corresponds to the second transition, and in general this is also a sharp transition, even though it does not correspond to any sharp change of property of the lubricant.

The second transition temperature depends to a large extent on the hardness of the contacting surfaces, on the strength of the lubricant-surface interaction, and on the sliding speed and geometry. The first transition, on the other hand, tends to be rather independent of such variables.

At temperatures above the second transition, the friction and wear take on values characteristic of unlubricated sliding. The lubricant does not appear to be influencing the sliding behavior in any way, even though it is visibly present on the surface.

Thus we must consider the behavior of lubricants in three regimes. The first regime is when the lubricant is present on the surface in *solid* form, below the first transition temperature. When the temperature is between the first and second transition the lubricant will be in the *liquid* phase, and this is the second stage. Last, above the second transition, the lubricant is in the *desorbed* stage. Since in the third stage the lubricant does not influence the frictional characteristics of the surfaces, we may confine our discussion of lubricant behavior to the first two stages.

8.6 Effectiveness of a Liquid Lubricant—
Intermediate Temperature

The ability of a liquid to function as a lubricant is determined by the magnitude of the interaction between its molecules and the sliding

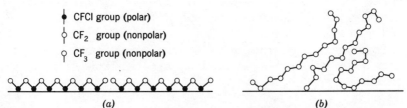

(a)   (b)

Fig. 8.15. (a) Schematic illustration of adsorption of $CF_3 - (CFCl\text{-}CF_2)_5 - CFCl - CF_3$. (b) Schematic illustration of adsorption of $CF_3(CF_2)_{11}CF_3$.

surfaces. As a general rule, liquids are good lubricants when they are polar and thus able to "grip" solid surfaces, and poor lubricants when they have low polarization. A typical pair of chemical substances which illustrates this distinction is seen in the chlorotrifluorohydrocarbons, of composition $CF_3(CF_2-CFCl)_nCF_3$, in contrast to the fully fluorinated hydrocarbons, $CF_3(CF_2)_mCF_3$. The former class of compounds is one of our most versatile families of lubricants, effective even on difficult-to-lubricate metals such as titanium and gold, because every second carbon atom has strong polarity. The latter family on the other hand, has very low polarity, and very low effectiveness as a lubricant (Fig. 8.15).

Besides the polarity of liquids, an important property which governs their effectiveness is the *shape* of their molecules, which determines whether they can form a dense, thick layer on the solid surface. Ring molecules tend to be much poorer than straight chain molecules, because there is no way in which they can achieve a really high packing density. Branch-chain molecules also are likely to produce a less dense film than can straight chain molecules. In some situations, especially at moderate temperatures, straight chain molecules with one polar end are highly desirable, because they enable a thick "carpet" to be formed, with the polar end tightly held on the surface and the rest of the molecule normal to the surface. The long-chain alcohols and soaps of fatty acids are typical representatives of this category (Fig. 8.16).

So far we have concerned ourselves with the properties of the liquid which makes it suitable or otherwise as a lubricant. We now turn to the properties of the solid surface which are helpful in allowing good lubrication. To be readily lubricated, a solid should have a high surface energy, so that there will be a strong tendency for molecules to adsorb on its surface. This means that metals tend to be the easiest

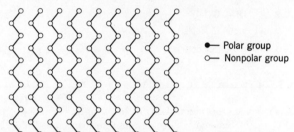

Fig. 8.16. Schematic illustration of adsorption by molecules with straight chains and one polar end.

surfaces to be lubricated, whereas non-metals, which tend to have low surface energies (Fig. 2.14), are much less easily lubricated.

Not only should the surface have a high surface energy, but it should be energetically compatible with the liquid lubricant, or else the lubricant molecules will have a low concentration on the surface. This compatibility is best revealed by the angle of wetting. If the liquid wets the solid, it will probably lubricate it. If it does not, it probably will not (Burwell, 1942; Imai and Rabinowicz, 1963).

8.7 Behavior of a Solid Lubricant—Temperature below Melting Point

The properties of a solid lubricant will be made up of two parts, those attributable to its attraction to the surface, and those arising from its mechanical properties, that is, the attraction of its molecules to each other. As a general rule, solid lubricant films are greatly superior to liquid films in giving better surface coverage and hence smaller values of α, but they do suffer from the serious fault that they tend to be worn away, whereupon the protection they provide is lost.

This tendency for wear may be combated in a number of ways. First, we may try to improve the wear resistance of a solid film by incorporating adhesives into it (e.g., epoxy resins in graphite or in teflon). Alternatively, we may arrange for a solid film to be formed continuously from a liquid or grease layer surrounding the surfaces.

This latter mode of behavior is utilized in lubrication by fatty acid soaps, which are widely used in metal deformation lubricants, and even more widely in greases. These materials form a strongly oriented film, which is replaced as necessary from the bulk liquid or grease.

In many cases the solid film is formed on the sliding surfaces by a chemical reaction. Thus, if a solution of a free fatty acid is used, it forms, on metal surfaces, a fatty soap with higher transition temperature and improved lubricating ability. Various chlorine, sulfur, and phosphorus compounds are also widely used as additives in lubricating oils, and under suitable conditions (usually a high temperature produced during sliding) solid films are formed, and these are re-formed continuously as they are worn away. The mode of action of these solid films is quite complex, and the oxide layers on the metal surface play an important role in increasing the effectiveness of the solid film (Vinogradov, Arkharova, and Petrov, 1961; Godfrey, 1962).

There have been a number of suggestions for vapor-phase lubricants to operate on the same principle (e.g., gaseous H_2S, to constitute the atmosphere surrounding a sliding system, and to form sulfides continuously). Many of these lubricants have been tried out, under laboratory conditions, and found to be effective.

8.8 Effect of Speed on Lubrication

Having considered the effect of temperatures on lubrication in the previous sections, we now move on to consider the effect of another important variable—speed. Basically, frictional phenomena are speed-independent (this, essentially, is the meaning of the third, or Coulomb, law of friction). Thus the friction coefficient is generally but little dependent on the speed (less than 10% variation of friction during a factor-of-10 change in sliding speed), whereas the wear rate is also reasonably independent of speed (less than a 50% variation of wear rate per unit distance of sliding, during a factor-of-10 change in sliding speed). The friction and wear sometimes increase and sometimes decrease, as the speed increases.

Apart from these relatively minor effects, there are three drastic speed effects which may be encountered. First, there is the effect due to frictional heating. The frictional heating will raise the surface temperature and thus the system may pass through a transition temperature with a great increase in friction and wear. Blok (1940) has shown that the temperature at which a transition takes place is the flash temperature over the real area of contact (see Section 4.12), not the ambient temperature of the surfaces. If the velocity is in the critical range, a factor-of-2 increase of sliding velocity may easily produce a factor-of-3 increase in friction and a factor-of-100 increase in wear. These values are to be contrasted with the far less marked dependencies considered above.

Alternatively, if a chemically active or E.P. lubricant is used, an

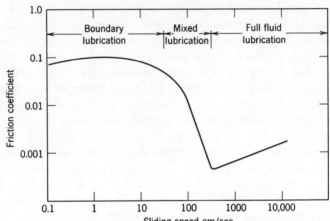

Fig. 8.17.   Friction-velocity curve for surfaces capable of hydrodynamic lubrication.

increase in temperature can promote an increase in chemical reaction, thus increasing corrosive wear while decreasing adhesive wear. In general, the onset of chemical reaction will tend to decrease the friction.

The second possible effect of a change in velocity is that of promoting a transition from boundary lubrication to full fluid lubrication. A typical friction-velocity curve is shown in Fig. 8.17, and it will be seen that this is one example of the familiar plot of friction against Sommerfeld number ZN/p. If the sliding velocity is high enough so that full fluid lubrication is achieved, friction is very low and wear is completely absent, and even at somewhat lower velocities, in the transitional or *mixed lubrication* region, both friction and wear may be greatly reduced, in relation to their magnitudes during boundary lubrication. Naturally, whether and when full fluid lubrication occurs is determined by variables such as sliding geometry, apparent pressure, viscosity, and surface roughness.

The third possible effect of speed is confined to repetitive sliding situations, where one surface repeatedly passes over the same spot on the other. Most lubricant films have the ability to heal themselves if damaged during sliding, but this healing process has associated with it a time-constant, and if the repetition rate is made too high, failure of the lubricant occurs.

8.9 Effect of Load on Lubrication

The situation in regard to this variable is rather similar to that of speed, as considered earlier. Nominally, the friction and wear coefficients are independent of load, and this is usually so in lightly loaded situations (for which the ratio of real area of contact A_r to apparent area A_a is less than about $\frac{1}{3}$, Burwell and Strang, 1952). However, at A_r/A_a values of above $\frac{1}{3}$, the friction and wear often increase markedly. This effect is rare when the lubricant film is solid, but very common when the film is liquid. In many cases the deterioration in lubrication arises from the fact that the junctions start to coalesce at high A_r/A_a values, and the lubricant may be unable to prevent this coalescing, which leads to galling.

At other times the effect of load is to raise the surface temperature by concentrating more frictional energy into a limited volume. This may lead to a temperature transition of the lubricant as considered previously. Another possibility is that the increase in load causes a failure in hydrodynamic lubrication. This, too, of course, will greatly increase friction and wear. Last, we must consider the possibility, present in repetitive sliding situations, that the sliding surfaces become so severely damaged, per revolution, that repair of the surface from the lubricant, before the next revolution, becomes impossible.

To sum up this section, generally an increase in load will lead to a proportional increase in the friction force and in the wear rate. There are complications, however, when the A_r/A_a ratio exceeds $\frac{1}{3}$, or in other special circumstances in which an increase in load has the same effect as an increase of speed. In fact, Fein (1960) shows that, in many circumstances, the transition from lower friction and wear to severe friction and wear occurs at a constant value of the load/speed ratio.

8.10 Lubricants and Their Properties

It is impossible within a limited space to do justice to this large and important topic. Here we shall merely enumerate the main types of lubricants and summarize their principal properties. For more detailed information, the reader is referred to the following books:

1. *Synthetic Lubricants*, ed. Gunderson and Hart (1962)
2. *Solid Lubricants and Surfaces*, Braithwaite (1964)
3. *Fuels and Lubricants*, Popovich and Hering (1959)

4. *Performance of Lubricating Oils*, Zuidema (1959)
5. *Lubricant Testing*, Ellis (1953)
6. *Lubrication and Friction*, Freeman (1962)

Perhaps some general comments are in order. In the case of solid film lubricants (Table 8.3), the graphite-molybdenum disulfide type in a binder is best in a majority of applications, the type of binder changing somewhat with the anticipated service conditions (must withstand high temperature, lubricating oil present, must resist corrosion by salt water, etc.).

The thickness of the film when applied is generally about 15 μ, which provides longest life. Thicker films apparently do not last as long (Crump, 1956), apparently because it becomes easier for wear particles consisting of the MoS_2-resin material to come off in loose form. In tests we have carried out on a thick block of a MoS_2-resin combination, we have found the average size of loose wear particles to be about 75 μ, and the minimum size to be about 20 μ. Thus, a film thickness somewhat below the size of the smallest wear particles seems logical.

Chemical coatings produced by phosphating, sulfiding, or anodizing give limited protection against severe surface damage, and are generally used in combination with other lubricants (Milne, 1957).

Turning now to liquid lubricants (Table 8.4), we find that no one type enjoys any innate superiority over the others. Hence, lubricants

Table 8.3. Types of Solid Film Lubricants

Type	Properties	Typical Uses
Graphite and/or MoS_2 + binder	Best general purpose lubricants. Low friction (0.12–0.06) reasonably long life (in range 10^4–10^6 cycles).	Locks and other intermittent mechanisms
Teflon + binder	Life not quite as long as previous type, but resistance to some liquids better.	As above
Rubbed graphite or MoS_2 film	Friction very low (0.10–0.04), but life quite short (10^2–10^4 cycles).	Deep drawing and other metalworking
Soft metal (lead, indium, cadmium)	Friction higher (0.30–0.15) and life not as long as resin-bonded types.	Running-in protection (temporary)
Phosphate Anodized film Other chemical coatings	Friction high (~ 0.20). Galling preventatives. Leave "spongy" surface layer.	Undercoating for resin-bonded film

Table 8.4. Types of Liquid Lubricants

Type	Properties	Typical Uses
Petroleum oils (mineral oils)	Basic lubrication ability fair, but additives produce great improvement. Poor lubrication action at high temperatures.	Very wide and general
Polyglycols	Quite good lubricants, do not form sludge on oxidizing.	Brake fluid
Silicones	Poor lubrication ability, especially against steel. Good thermal stability	Rubber seals. Mechanical dampers
Chlorofluorocarbons	Good lubricants, good thermal stability.	Oxygen compressors. Chemical processing equipment
Polyphenyl ethers	Very wide liquid range. Excellent thermal stability. Fair lubricating ability.	High temperature sliding systems
Phosphate esters	Good lubricants—E.P. action	Hydraulic fluid + lubricant
Dibasic esters	Good lubricating properties. Can stand higher temperatures than mineral oils.	Jet engines

from several families should be tested. It is my experience that engineers who have encountered lubrication problems, because of the use of novel materials or conditions of sliding, tend to restrict themselves unnecessarily in their selection of lubricants (for example, after unsuccessfully trying a mineral oil manufactured by one large oil company, they try a rather similar mineral oil produced by another). This procedure is not likely to be successful. Instead some of the synthetics should be tried.

References

Barwell, F. T., and A. A. Milne (1951), The Lubrication of Rough Steel Surfaces by a Series of Metallic Soaps, *Brit. J. Appl. Phys.*, Suppl. **1**, 44–48.
Blok, H. (1940), Fundamental Mechanical Aspects of Boundary Lubrication, *S.A.E. Trans.*, **46**, 54–68.
Bowden, F. P., J. N. Gregory, and D. Tabor (1945), Lubrication of Metal Surfaces by Fatty Acids, *Nature*, **156**, 97–101.
Braithwaite, E. R. (1964), *Solid Lubricants and Surfaces*, Pergamon. New York.

Burwell, J. T. (1942), The Role of Surface Chemistry and Profile in Boundary Lubrication, S.A.E. Journal, 50, 450–457.

Burwell, J. T., and C. D. Strang (1952), On the Empirical Law of Adhesive Wear, J. Appl. Phys., 23, 18–28.

Campbell, W. E., and R. E. Lee (1962), Polymer Formation on Sliding Metals in Air Saturated with Organic Vapors, Trans. Am. Soc. Lubrication Eng., 5, 91–104.

Crump, R. E. (1956), Solid Film Lubricants—Factors Influencing Their Mechanism of Friction and Wear, Am. Soc. Lubr. Eng., Paper 56 LC-8.

Ellis, E. G. (1953), Lubricant Testing, Scientific Publications (Great Britain), London.

Fein, R. S. (1960), Transition Temperatures with Four Ball Machines, Trans. Am. Soc. Lubrication Eng., 3, 34–39.

Finkin, E. (1962), Surface Roughness in Wear, B.S. Thesis in Mechanical Engineering, M.I.T.

Freeman, P. (1962), Lubrication and Friction, Pitman, London.

Godfrey, D. (1962), Chemical Changes in Steel Surfaces during Extreme Pressure Lubrication, Trans. Am. Soc. Lubrication Eng., 5, 57–66.

Gunderson, R. C., and A. W. Hart (eds.) (1962), Synthetic Lubricants, Reinhold, New York.

Hermance, H. W., and Egan, T. F. (1958), Organic Deposits on Precious Metal Contacts, Bell System Tech. J., 37, 739–772.

Huttig, G. F., and H. Sales (1956), The Grinding of Metal Powders, pp. 8–10 of Symposium on Powder Metallurgy, Special Report No. 58, Iron and Steel Institute, London.

Imai, M., and E. Rabinowicz (1963), Lubrication by Low-Melting-Point Metals at Elevated Temperatures, Trans. Am. Soc. Lubrication Eng., 6, 286–294.

Levine, O., and W. A. Zisman (1957), Friction and Wettability of Aliphatic Polar Compounds and Effect of Halogenation, J. Phys. Chem., 61, 1068–1077.

Milne, A. A. (1957), Experiments on the Friction and Endurance of Various Surface Treatments Lubricated by Molybdenum Disulfide, Wear, 1, 92–103.

Nagata, S., Y. Tomoda, and H. Haga (1956), A Study of Lubrication of Aromatic Compounds (in French), Tech. Rep. Osaka Univ., 6, 31–42.

Popovich, M., and C. Hering (1959), Fuels and Lubricants, Wiley, New York.

Rabinowicz, E., and D. Tabor (1951), Metallic Transfer between Sliding Metals— an Autoradiographic Study, Proc. Roy. Soc., A 208, 455–475.

Rabinowicz, E. (1958), Boundary Lubrication of Titanium, Proc. of Fifth World Petroleum Congress, 6, 319–330.

Rabinowicz, E., and R. G. Foster (1963), New Methods of Evaluating Lubricants Based on the Surface Energy/Hardness Ratio, S.A.E. Paper 776 A.

Rabinowicz, E., and R. G. Foster (1964), Effect of Surface Energy on the Wear Process, Trans. A.S.M.E., 86 D, 306–310.

Tamai, Y., and B. G. Rightmire (1965), Mechanism of Boundary Lubrication and the Edge Effect, Trans. A.S.M.E., 87D, 735–740.

Tyagi, S. K. (1963), Particle Sizes Produced by Ball-Milling, S.M. Thesis in Mechanical Engineering, M.I.T.

Vinogradov, G. V., V. V. Arkharova, and A. A. Petrov (1961), Anti-Wear and Anti-Friction Properties of Hydrocarbons under Heavy Loads, Wear, 4, 274–291.

Zuidema, H. H. (1959), Performance of Lubricating Oils, 2nd ed., Reinhold, New York.

9

Adhesion

9.1 Introduction

Adhesion, the last of the surface interaction phenomena we shall consider in this volume, is the one which has been studied the least. In spite of this fact, or perhaps because of it, a number of good comprehensive review articles and books are available (Zisman, 1963; Milner and Rowe, 1962; Weiss, 1962; and Eley, 1961). Adhesion is the phenomenon which occurs when we press two surfaces together, either under a pure normal load or else under combined normal and shear forces, and then find that a normal tension force must be exerted to separate the surfaces (Fig. 9.1). [*Note:* There is a different phenomenon, also called adhesion, which involves the use of tacky solids or liquids (see, for example Bikerman, 1961). This will not be considered here.] The ratio of normal tensile force L' required for separation to normal compressive force L initially applied, is often referred to as the coefficient of adhesion, or f', that is,

$$f' = \frac{L'}{L} \tag{9.1}$$

Under ordinary conditions, there are very few materials which are subject to adhesion to any marked degree (chewing gum, modeling clay, carefully cleaned indium), and accordingly we tend to regard adhesion as anomalous behavior which requires explanation. But this is a misstatement of the true position. In general, two solid bodies situated adjacent to each other will adhere. Thus, in a polycrystalline material, which consists of a number of abutting crystals, the various

221

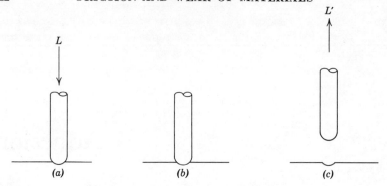

Fig. 9.1.   Schematic illustration of adhesion.   (a) Compressive forces applied; (b) Force removed; (c) tensile force needed to separate surfaces.

crystals adhere quite firmly to each other, with but seldom any indication of weakening due to the presence of grain boundaries.   This strong adhesion is found in two-phase alloys, in which adjoining grains differ in composition, as well as in single-phase materials, in which adjacent grains have the same composition.

Further evidence for the strong tendencies of solids to adhere is found in the process of adhesive wear.   As we have seen, adhesive wear cannot be explained unless strong adhesive forces are assumed to exist between contacting solids; and yet adhesive wear occurs universally.   Accordingly, we must ask, not why adhesion sometimes occurs, but rather, why it occurs so seldom!

The answer to this paradox lies in three characteristic phenomena which we have encountered before, namely the small value of the real area of contact, the tendency for surfaces to become contaminated, and the tendency for adhesive joints to be broken up by residual elastic stress.   All these serve to diminish the magnitude of adhesive effects, and it may be shown that the last of these is the most important factor.

Suppose we press a hemispherically ended rider against a flat surface under a load, and then remove the load.   The appearance of the surfaces will be as shown in Fig. 9.2.   While the load is applied the two surfaces conform over the area of the indentation, but as soon as the load is removed the elastic stresses cause the two bodies to take up different radii of curvature and the real area of contact becomes quite small.

We may consider a simple example in which a steel rider, of radius 3 mm, is pressed by a 1 kg load against a steel flat.   Suppose the radius of curvature of the flat is 6 mm after the load is removed.   Then we can calculate the residual area of contact, which we may define as that area over which the separation of the surfaces is less than some small distance of atomic dimensions, for example 3×10^{-8} cm.

Referring to Fig. 9.2, we have to a good degree of approximation,

$$AF = \frac{DF^2}{2r} = \frac{DF^2}{0.6 \text{ cm}}$$

$$AB = \frac{DF^2}{2R} = \frac{DF^2}{1.2 \text{ cm}}$$

$$AF - AB = 3 \times 10^{-8} \text{ cm} = \frac{DF^2}{1.2 \text{ cm}} \tag{9.2}$$

From this we find that $DF = 1.9 \times 10^{-4}$ cm, and that the residual area A' is 1.1×10^{-7} cm^2.

If the hardness of the steel is taken to be 2×10^{10} dyne/cm^2 and we assume that the residual area has as great a resistance to being broken in tension as it would have for plastic deformation in compression, we can apply the standard equation

$$L' = A'p \tag{9.3}$$

and thus we find that the force required to break up the residual area of contact is about 2200 dynes or 2 gm. This would give a coefficient of adhesion f' of $2g/1$ kg or 0.002.

At first sight it would appear that much higher values of adhesion coefficient could be attained by pressing flat surfaces together; but if

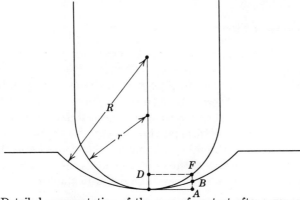

Fig. 9.2. Detailed representation of the area of contact after compressive force has been removed.

these are the nominally flat surfaces which were discussed in Chapter 3, contact will be at just a few points of rather small radius of curvature, each of which will give a very small residual area of contact. The overall residual area is likely to be of the same order of magnitude as that obtained with a hemisphere on a flat surface.

Next, we might suppose that high values of coefficient of adhesion might be observed at light loads, since the residual area A' is independent of load according to the oversimplified model we have considered previously, and since the coefficient of adhesion is given by

$$f' = \frac{L'}{L} = \frac{pA'}{L} \tag{9.4}$$

we see that f' is inversely proportional to L.

Under some circumstances, high values of f' can indeed be observed at low loads. But two factors exist which reduce f' at light loads. One of these is vibration of the contacting surfaces which tends to break up the residual area of contact, especially when bodies of high inertia are pressed together under a light load or a zero load. The other of these effects, which prevents adhesion becoming prominent for lightly loaded contacts, is the presence of contamination on the surfaces. Any contaminant layers on the surfaces greatly reduce the extent of adhesion. At high loads, some shear of the interface occurs, and this serves to break through the contaminant layer. At low loads the contaminant layer is fully effective.

Under some circumstances, however, the presence of contaminants can itself cause adhesive effects. This takes place when the contaminant is liquid, and hence surface tension forces come into play. We consider this phenomenon next.

9.2 Adhesion Effects Produced by Surface Tension

If a hemispherical surface is pressed against a flat surface, and a drop of liquid is introduced at the point of contact (Fig. 9.3), surface tension effects will arise. The surface tension will attempt to pull the surfaces closer together; furthermore, surface tension will resist separation of the surfaces in a direction normal to the interface. This is because, whenever surface tension acts, the pressure inside the liquid is lower than it is outside the liquid by an amount γ/r' (where r' is the radius of curvature of the surface of the liquid, and γ is the surface tension), and hence the adhesive force L' can be written in the form

$$L' = \frac{\pi r^2 \gamma}{r'} \tag{9.5}$$

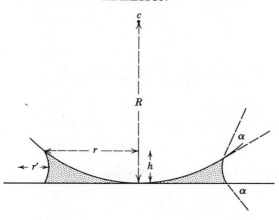

Fig. 9.3. The geometry of contact when a liquid drop is in the region of contact between a curved and a flat surface.

Now if the amount of liquid is small so that its top and bottom surfaces may be assumed to be essentially parallel, we have

$$r' = \frac{h}{2 \cos \alpha} \tag{9.6}$$

where α is the angle of contact between liquid and solid.

Also, geometric considerations show that

$$r^2 = 2Rh \text{ approx.} \tag{9.7}$$

Combining eq. 9.7 with eq. 9.6 and 9.5 gives

$$L' = 4\pi R\gamma \cos \alpha \tag{9.8}$$

It will be seen that the force of adhesion is independent of the amount of liquid at the interface, since the parameter r' does not appear in the expression for L'.

To get a feel for the order of magnitude of the adhesive force represented in eq. 9.8, we may consider a concrete example, in which a drop of water ($\gamma = 70$ dynes/cm) is introduced into the region of contact of a $\frac{1}{4}$-in. hemispherically ended rider which is touching a flat plate. If we assume perfect wetting between the water and the two solid surfaces ($\cos \alpha = 1$), we find that L' has a value of 275 dynes or 0.28 gm.

Although the surface tension force turns out to be small in the example just considered, it can become large when we consider the contact of two flat surfaces ($R \to \infty$). For a flat disc of radius r in

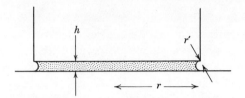

Fig. 9.4. Two flat surfaces separated by a thin liquid film.

contact with a flat surface, we have (Fig. 9.4)

$$L' = \frac{\pi r^2 \gamma}{r'} \qquad (9.9)$$

This is to be combined with eq. 9.6 to yield

$$L' = \frac{2\pi r^2 \gamma \cos \alpha}{h} \qquad (9.10)$$

As a practical example, let us assume that we bring together two flat, well-polished discs of diameter 1 in., and that a very small quantity of oil ($\gamma = 30$ dynes/cm) is introduced into the interface. If the oil is perfectly clean and contains no suspended particles larger than $\frac{1}{4} \mu$, we should be able to bring the surfaces together with a separation of that amount, that is, 10^{-5} in. For this system we may compute a value for L' of 2.8×10^7 dynes, or no less than 62 lb. Actually, it might not be necessary to apply a force as large as this to separate the surfaces. The liquid would have a tendency to cavitate (boil locally) at a negative pressure exceeding atmospheric, especially if it contained appreciable amounts of dissolved air or other volatile substances. Also, if the viscosity of the oil is appreciable, it would take an appreciable time to affect separation of the surfaces, even if the force L' were enough to overcome surface tension. The effect of neither cavitation nor viscosity, however, can change the fact that large adhesive forces can exist with flat surfaces separated by a very thin liquid film.

The surface tension effect considered above is the basis for the strong adhesion observed when gage blocks, consisting of very flat surfaces covered by thin films of oil and grease, are pressed together. Many people regard this adhesion as being produced by solid-to-solid adhesive forces, but this may be disproved in two different ways. First, if we carefully degrease the gage blocks, they will not adhere when we "wring" or twist them together (they will damage each other severely, but that is another story); second, if we immerse a strongly adhering pair of gage blocks in oil, the adhesion becomes very small, because the oil-to-air surface with very small radius of curvature has disappeared.

Comparing the adhesive effects observed with liquids with those observed with solids, we note with some surprise that in the presence of thin films of liquid the adhesive effects are far greater. This seems anomalous, but the explanation is simple. When the liquid is present, the area covered by the liquid, and affected by it, will tend to be large, while in the absence of the liquid the real area of contact is very small. Furthermore, the liquid stores no elastic energy, and thus is not subject to the breaking of junctions when an initial compressive force is removed.

9.3 Adhesive Effects Produced by Purely Normal Contact

In this section, we consider the adhesive effects which arise during the purely normal contact of dry surfaces, in the absence of tangential displacement. Several well-established examples of this pure adhesion may be cited. Thus, when mica crystals are partially cleaved, and the cleaved portions are then allowed to reunite, they will adhere with nearly their original strength (Bailey, 1961). Other cleaved materials behave similarly.

It must be stated, however, that, generally, when two nominally flat surfaces (as opposed to the atomically flat mica surfaces just considered) are pressed together by a purely normal load, the amount of adhesion is generally very small. The first and foremost reason for this is the very small value of the real area of contact, resulting from an initially small area when the normal load is applied, and then a drastic reduction when the normal load is removed and residual stresses come into play. The presence of contaminant and other films is generally a contributing factor in producing poor adhesion, since these films often have much lower tensile strengths than do the bulk solids which are in contact.

We may illustrate this influence of contaminants by referring to the case of cleaved mica. If a lubricant film is introduced into the system, on either surface, the adhesion on subsequent placing together of the surfaces drops off drastically, by about a factor of 10.

To achieve good adhesion during the normal contact of clean surfaces, we have to find some way of reducing the residual stresses and their harmful effects. One very effective way is to use a material with a low elastic modulus and a low elastic maximum strain. Among the metals, indium is outstanding in both categories, and can be made to adhere fairly easily to other materials, as long as both materials are free from grease-type contaminants. A number of materials that straddle the borderline between solid and liquid (modeling clay, chewing gum, glue) are even better.

A second way of overcoming residual stresses is to use a material with a pronounced creep rate. Even though the stored elastic energy is high when the two specimens are first pressed together, creep occurs with the dual effect of increasing the real area of contact and decreasing the elastic energy. If the surfaces are kept in contact for a reasonable length of time and the normal force is then removed, strong adhesion will have occurred. Unfortunately, it is hard to separate this effect from that considered above since the type of material that shows pronounced creep tends to be the same as that which shows low elastic stresses and strains, namely soft metals and Bingham solids of the chewing gum type. Pronounced creep is also observed, however, with hard metals at elevated temperatures (with the absolute temperature of the metal exceeding half its melting temperature on the absolute scale). Experiments show that metals do indeed show appreciable adhesion at these elevated temperatures (Bowden and Rowe, 1956). Observations on the increase of the adhesion of lead with loading time are made by Ling and Weiner (1961).

A third method of achieving good adhesion is to use one of the materials in the form of a thin sheet, rather than a massive block. In this system elastic stresses cannot build up to very high values, and hence elastic spring-back is minimized. This method has not been much investigated.

The foregoing methods are all rather specialized. There is, however, a general method of increasing the real area of contact during the loading stage, and this involves combining a shear force with the normal force, thus producing slip or sliding at the interface.

9.4 Adhesive Effects after Compression Plus Shear

It is well known that adhesive effects can be greatly increased if the normal load is supplemented by a shear displacement of the interface. Thus, even in the simple experiment in which a steel rod is pressed into a freshly cut (and hence clean) indium surface (Fig. 9.5), it is found that the adhesion is much greater if the rod is twisted after being pressed into the indium. Alternatively, we may produce increased adhesion by sliding the rod along the indium surface (McFarlane and Tabor, 1950).

Sikorski (1963) has carried out experiments in which the flat ends of hollowed cylindrical specimens were pressed together, then twisted

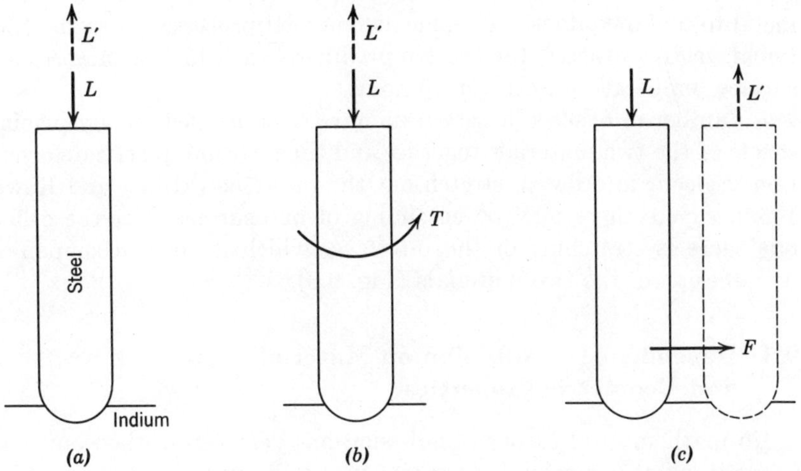

L'

L

Steel

Indium

(a)

L'

L

T

(b)

L

L'

F

(c)

Fig. 9.5. Three ways of measuring the adhesion between steel and indium.
(*a*) Load applied normally. Adhesion moderate. (*b*) Load and twist applied
together. Adhesion good. (*c*) Load and shear force applied together. Adhesion
good.

together, and then the adhesion was measured. In this case, too,
adhesion was observed only after a considerable degree of twisting, but
it was observed that even metals as hard as nickel showed a reasonably
high adhesion coefficient (0.4).

In these press-and-shear experiments the sliding performs two functions; first, it leads to an increase in the real area of contact, and
second, it tends to produce penetration of surface layers which prevent

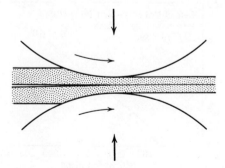

Fig. 9.6. Roll-bonding method of producing adhesion (combined normal stress
and interface stretch.

metal to metal contact.   In some commercial processes (e.g., the frictional welding process) the friction produces heat which then raises the surface temperature to the creep point.

A number of other adhesion tests have been carried out by placing sheets of the two materials together and then causing plastic deformation to occur in order to stretch out the interface (Milner and Rowe, 1962).   Here there may be no sliding of one surface over the other, but there is stretching of the interface, which is then accompanied by adhesion of the two materials (Fig. 9.6).

9.5   Dependence of Adhesion on Material and Geometric Properties

No mathematical theory of adhesion has yet been worked out, and hence it is not yet possible to compute the amount of adhesion which may be expected in any particular case.   Also, it is not very easy to identify the important parameters by considering the experimental data which are available, because of the strong correlation between many of the mechanical parameters.   Thus it is clear that a soft metal like lead adheres far better than does a hard metal like nickel.   But this may be because lead has a lower recrystallization temperature, or a lower Young's modulus, or a lower elastic strain, or a lower hardness.

It is clear, however, that adhesion is high when we use materials with a high surface energy, since this will make it more difficult for a junction to be broken; also, adhesion will be high if our materials can store small amounts of elastic energy only, since this will reduce elastic springback.   In earlier chapters we have frequently encountered

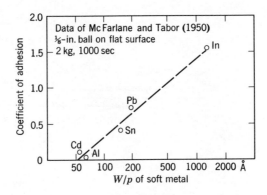

Fig. 9.7.   Adhesion during load-unload testing.

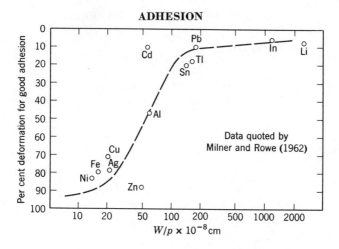

Fig. 9.8.   Adhesion during roll-bonding.

situations in which a surface energy was counteracted by a volume energy, and we found that the parameter W/p represented the balance between these forms of energy.   Accordingly, we will attempt to correlate the adhesive properties of materials with their W/p ratios.

Three sets of adhesion data are correlated with the W/p ratios of the contacting materials in Figs. 9.7, 9.8, and 9.9.   Figure 9.7 represents the coefficient of adhesion when a clean steel ball of diameter $\frac{1}{8}$ in. is pressed into a clean flat surface for 1000 sec.   Figure 9.8 shows the least amount of per cent deformation during pressure welding that will produce good adhesion, the data being taken from data quoted in Table I of Milner and Rowe, (1962).   Last, Fig. 9.9 shows the very extensive data of Sikorski (1963) obtained during the compression-twisting of the ends of hollow cylinders.   This last curve shows very clearly the effect of crystal structure superposed on the effect of the W/p ratio, with hexagonal metals giving the least adhesion and cubic metals giving the most.   The other curves appear to be similar, but there may be differences due to the special conditions of the tests. In Fig. 9.7, cadmium may be giving more adhesion than aluminum because its melting point is lower, and hence the creep at room temperature will be more pronounced, which might show up in a test lasting 1000 sec.

It must be admitted, however, that a plot of adhesion against hardness alone would give just as good correlation as a plot against the W_{ab}/p ratio.   Failing theoretical expressions for the adhesive process as a whole, we are unable to find which factors are really involved.

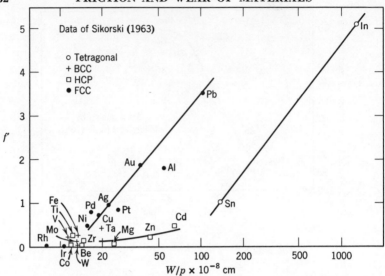

Fig. 9.9. Adhesion during compression-twisting.

It is significant, however, that Keller (1963) finds adhesion far more pronounced with unlike metal pairs which form an intermediate phase than with those which are insoluble. Since insoluble metals have smaller values of W_{ab} than do soluble metals, this suggests that the work of adhesion has a part in determining coefficients of adhesion.

As regards the effect of geometry, it is clear that a geometry which makes it easy for the real area of contact to grow is to be preferred over a geometry which makes junction growth difficult. The ideally flat mica surfaces achieve maximum area of contact merely by being placed together. Sikorski, pressing and sliding flat surfaces together, was able to get good adhesion with metals as hard as gold and aluminum, whereas McFarlane and Tabor, using a hemisphere on a flat, found it very difficult to get good adhesion when sliding on a metal as soft as lead. Perhaps the angle at the termination of the junction is a parameter which should appear in an expression for coefficient of adhesion, just as it does in the expression for coefficient of friction (*cf.* eq. 4.8).

9.6 Adhesion of Lubricated and of Outgassed Surfaces

If indeed the adhesion does depend on the W/p ratio of the contacting surfaces, we are in the position to estimate the effect of applying a good lubricant, or, in the other direction, to estimate the effect of carrying out adhesion tests on very clean materials in a high vacuum. In the first case, we note that good lubricants lower W by factors of 10 or 20, which will be enough to reduce the adhesion to negligibly low values in most cases. In the second case, we might expect that clean metals in a high vacuum will have values of W larger than those of clean metals in air by factors of 2 or 3, probably, and this will produce large but generally not order-of-magnitude increases of adhesion.

These predictions appear to be borne out by what little experimental data is available in the published literature.

References

Bailey, A. I. (1961), Friction and Adhesion of Clean and Contaminated Mica Surfaces, *J. Appl. Phys.*, **32**, 1407–1412.

Bikerman, J. J. (1961), *The Science of Adhesive Joints*, Academic Press, New York.

Bowden, F. P., and G. W. Rowe (1956), The Adhesion of Clean Metals, *Proc. Roy. Soc.*, **A 233**, 429–442.

Eley, D. D. (ed.) (1961), *Adhesion*, Oxford University Press, Oxford.

Milner, D. R., and G. W. Rowe (1962), Fundamentals of Solid Phase Welding, *Metallurgical Rev.*, **7**, 433–480.

McFarlane, J. S., and D. Tabor (1950), Adhesion of Solids and the Effect of Surface Films, *Proc. Roy. Soc.* **A 202**, 224–243.

Keller, D. V. (1963), Adhesion between Solid Metals, *Wear*, **6**, 353–365.

Sikorski, M. (1963), Correlation of the Coefficient of Adhesion with Various Physical and Mechanical Properties of Metals, *Trans. A.S.M.E.*, **D 85**, 279–285.

Weiss, P. (ed.) (1962), *Adhesion and Cohesion*, Elsevier, Amsterdam.

Zisman, W. A. (1963), Adhesion, *Ind. Eng. Chem.*, **55**, No. 10, 19–38.

Appendix

This appendix tabulates some of the physical and mechanical properties of the materials which are discussed in Chapter 2. The data for melting temperature and Young's modulus are reasonably well established, and fortunately are not greatly affected by the exact structure of the material, provided the material is in an isotropic form. The yield stress (0.2% plastic strain) and hardness are, however, greatly affected by the structure of the material, and wherever possible, I have tried to choose data for pure materials in the fully cold worked condition. For many of the rare metals, the values quoted are for metal which may differ quite markedly from this ideal. Also, metals like chromium and rhodium are generally met with in the form of electrodeposits, and the metals in that form may be quite brittle and have hardness values as much as a factor of four greater than the values given in Table A.1.

The surface energy data are for the pure material, in an inert environment, at the melting point of the material. Although surface energy values as thus defined are structure independent, there are severe difficulties in determining them, and many of the values quoted are subject to errors of $\pm 25\%$.

Table A.1. Properties of Metallic Elements

Metal	Melting Temp. °C	Young's Modulus E 10^{12} dyne/cm²	Yield Strength σ_y 10^9 dyne/cm²	Hardness p kg/mm²	Surface Energy γ erg/cm²	γ/p 10^{-8} cm
Aluminum	660	0.63	1.1	27	900	33
Antimony	630	0.80	0.11 f	58	370	6.4
Beryllium	1400	3.0	3.2	150	1000	6.7
Bismuth	270	0.32		7	390	56
Cadmium	321	0.56	0.72	22	620	28
Calcium	838	0.25	0.87	17		
Cerium	804	0.30	1.2	48		
Cesium	29					
Chromium	1875	2.6	1.6	125		
Cobalt	1495	2.1	7.8	125	1530?	12
Copper	1083	1.2	3.2	80	1100	14
Dysprosium	1407	0.63	3.3	117		
Erbium	1496	0.75	2.9	161		
Europium	827			17		
Gadolinium	1312	0.56	2.7	97		
Gallium	30			6.5	360	55
Germanium	937	1.56				
Gold	1063	0.81	2.1	58	1120	19
Hafnium	2222		2.4	260		
Holmium	1461	0.68	2.2	90		
Indium	156	0.11	0.03	0.9		
Iridium	2454	5.4	6.3	350		
Iron	1534	2.04	2.5	82	1500	18
Lanthanum	930	0.39	1.9	150		
Lead	325	0.16	0.09	4	450	110
Lithium	180				400	
Lutetium	1652			118		
Magnesium	650	0.44	1.5	46	560	12
Manganese	1245		2.5 f	300		
Mercury	−39				460	
Molybdenum	2610	3.0	8.4	240		
Neodymium	1018	0.38	1.7	80		
Nickel	1453	2.08	3.2	210	1700	8.1
Niobium	2468	1.05	2.8	160	2100	13
Osmium	2700	5.7		800	1190?	1.5
Palladium	1552	1.15	3.1	110		
Platinum	1769	1.50	1.6	100	1800	18
Plutonium	640	0.99	2.8	266		
Potassium	64			0.04	86	2300
Praseodymium	919	0.35	2.0	76		
Rhenium	3180	4.70	22			
Rhodium	1966	2.96	9.7	122		
Rubidium	39					
Ruthenium	2500	4.22	5.5	390		
Samarium	1072	0.35	1.3	64		
Scandium	1540					
Silver	961	0.78	2.0	80	920	11
Sodium	98			0.07	200	2800
Tantalum	2996	1.90	3.5			
Terbium	1356	0.58		88		
Thallium	303		0.09	2	400	200
Thorium	1750	1.47	1.5	37		
Thulium	1545		1.4	53		
Tin	232	0.44	0.15	5.3	570	110
Titanium	1670	1.13	1.4	65		
Tungsten	3410	3.51	18	435	2300	5.3
Uranium	1132	1.69	2.0			
Vanadium	1900	1.34	8.4			
Ytterbium	824	0.18	0.73	21		
Yttrium	1495	0.66	1.4	37		
Zinc	420	0.91	1.3	38	790	21
Zirconium	1852	0.96	2.0	145		

Sources of Data

Melting temperature Young's modulus Yield strength	Main source: *Metals Handbook*, Vol. 1, ASM, 1961. Subsidiary source: *Handbook of Chemistry and Physics*, 44th edition, Chemical Rubber Publishing Co., Cleveland, 1963. Some data were taken from other publications.
Hardness	Main sources as above. A number of data were taken from D. Tabor, *The Hardness of Metals*, Oxford, 1951.
Surface Energy	Main source: V. K. Semenchenko, *Surface Phenomena in Metals and Alloys*, Addison-Wesley, Reading, Mass., 1962. Subsidiary reference: *Metals Handbook*, Vol. 1, ASM, 1961. Some data were taken from other publications.

Table A.2.   Surface Energy Data for Non-Metals

Material	Surface Energy erg/cm^2	Hardness p, kg/mm^2	$\gamma/p, 10^{-8}$cm
AgCl	100	9	11
Al$_2$O$_3$	740	2150	0.34
BaF$_2$	210		
CaCO$_3$	170	120	1.4
CaF$_2$	340		
CdO	360		
KCl	85	35	2.4
LiF	260	100	2.6
MgO	670	500	1.3
Mica	250	40	6.2
Si	930		
ThO	310		
TiC	900	2400	0.38
UC	750		
UO$_2$	415		
VC	1250	2500	0.50
ZnO	400		
ZrC	600	2100	0.28
ZrO$_2$	530	1150	0.46

Sources: For Surface Energies: —Livesey, D. T. and Murray, P. (1956) The Surface Energies of Solid Oxides and Carbides, *J. Am. Ceram. Soc.*, **39,** 363–372; Gilman, J. J. (1960) Direct Measurements of the Surface Energies of Crystals, *J. App. Phys.*, **31,** 2208–2218.

For Hardness Values: Mott, B. W. (1956) *Micro-Indentation Hardness Testing,* Butterworths, London.

Author Index

237

Subject Index